Roberta S. Herzog

ANCIENT WIZDOM
STORIES

All the best —

Roberta S Herzog

Words of Wizdom

International, Inc.

ISBN 1-884695-08-6

Printed in the United States of America

For information on quantity discounts to the trade and to libraries, kindly write to the Publisher:

Words of Wizdom International, Inc.
P.O. Box 4347
Boca Raton, FL 33429
USA
Phone: (407) 997-9795
Fax: (407) 997-2243

Publisher's Message:

At several points throughout this book, you will see words joined together and spelled in an uncommon manner. You will also find capital letters in unlikely places, the intent being to emphasize the importance of a particular word.

In editing the text, we decided to leave Roberta's vivid writing style intact, in lieu of syntax and editorial correctness. Therefore, we hope you enjoy her unique way of conveying these stories to you. Her style of writing is very visual. She makes the words and the way the words are set to paper speak to you, the reader, and therefore these words readily come to life. We hope you enjoy her creative style as much as the stories.

TABLE OF CONTENTS:

The First Portal

The Second Portal

DEDICATION

My dear husband Nicholas, to whom "Legends of Anelleh" was formally dedicated in 1982, passed from this earthly life to the higher reality in 1992, exactly ten years after Anelleh made her first appearance on bookshelves. Nicholas encouraged the writing of these stories as he always said they brought to Light many Truths. This new edition of "Legends of Anelleh" now has added stories that I know he would have been pleased to read.

A lovely lady named Kay Basiura has been a long time friend of both Nicholas and myself. Kay has always shown sincere, loving and heartfelt interest in my work over the more than twenty years of association. She is a devoted student of Metaphysics and an outstanding gardener of flowers and all kinds of wonderful vegetables. However, it is the Garden of Her Soul that is so beautiful... thank you, Kay, for many years of love and encouragement to me.

To you both... Nicholas and Kay, this new edition is lovingly dedicated. Thank you both for being in my life.

Preface

In this book, are questions you will ask and must answer for yourself. Are the stories dredged from the long distant past of Roberta's Cosmic Mind, recalled from her travels astrally, or yet again just a product of her very fertile creative mind? I know you will be entertained and intrigued, but most of all, you will learn. It will, I am sure, be one of the most pleasant educational experiences of your life. Each story is pregnant with mystical, metaphysical lessons woven into a loving tapestry of enchantment for you... her brothers and sisters upon the Path.

To me, Roberta is a true, natural genius. Now, one can conjure up a cold, sterile personality with that description. She is anything but! She is beautiful inside and out, the sister I never had, my beloved friend, a dedicated, brilliant teacher, a true servant of our Father/Mother God, and she has chosen our Church as her instrument of Service. The Church and her fellow men and women have benefited. She is the Director of our Church's Esoteric Seminary & College, Administrator of our Church's Office, the Editor of "Aquarian Lights" magazine, a gifted designer of clothes and jewelry, a fabulous portrait artist, a wonderful wife to her beloved Nicholas, a great cook and sometimes plays vet to her large family of farm animals. She is many things to many people. To me, she is my little Sister...

Muriel E. Hand
Archbishop Primate
The International Church of Ageless Wisdom
1982

FOREWORD...

Loving thoughts sincerely shared can be a Blessing both for the giver and the receiver. I have found, in over twenty-one years in the metaphysical and Spiritual Work, that it was very dull and sometimes quite boring to continually read straight texts, however profoundly written. There has always been something about the story form that has not only kept my attention but has keyed me into subjects that later became a lifelong interest... and yes, many, many texts have been read between stories but the sparkling rainbows in a tale brought me into the consciousness of the writer and into the heart and soul of the teachings. Perhaps you have found this to be true too...

The Anelleh stories came to manifestation after a deeply illuminating Inner experience in southern California in the Spring of 1980. This experience was personal and sacred. However, as the months passed and I returned home to my mountain in northeastern Pennsylvania, there began to grow in my mind the thought that others, throughout history, had not only had beautiful Inner experiences but that they too had been contacted, consciously, by the Ancient Mystical White Brotherhood and that these experiences needed to be shared.

I began to tell these stories verbally at conferences sponsored by the Church into which I have taken my Ordination, The International Church of Ageless Wisdom. The responses were very touching and meaningful to me. I therefore continued to tell several additional stories at the end of day-long workshops with equally sustaining acceptance. Upon the encouragement of many people to put them into one place, this volume is the reflection of those urgings.

Several people have asked me, "Who is Anelleh?", and "Who is Little One?". Throughout the five stories, you will be able to piece together an outline of Anelleh. This is a woman who learned the secrets of longevity through her studies with the Brotherhood and, at the time of her physical transition, was over two hundred years old. She was commanded to keep the silence about her adventures around the world until seven years prior to her transition. Let the characters be a small reflection of something Inside you. Let the stories be the mystical allegories they were written to be... truths conveyed in an interesting manner.

To each of you who are impressed to read all of my stories, please accept my appreciation. May each of you be blessed abundantly with peace of mind, good health and prosperity in every area of your life.

In the Service of the One,

Roberta S. Herzog

Wyalusing, Pennsylvania
1994

The First

Portal

First Questions ...

Eternal Truths

*J*ust about one year before she went into physical transition, I had the opportunity to ask Anelleh how she came into contact with the Brotherhood. What she told me has remained Within me to this day. The story is a lovely one... it is not only Anelleh's story but in many ways it is our story...

We were sitting on her back porch, overlooking the trees and flowers she had cultivated for many years. As always there was a meditative silence between us before she told me of her wondrous adventures in the Mystery Schools of many countries. With those deep, black eyes, eyes that seemed to see clear through me, she gazed at my face lovingly, tenderly... as a mother might look at her child. She then began this story in answer to my question...

"Little One, it's been a long time since I have thought about the first instance my thoughts wandered toward the mystical side of life... I must think... I know I was only a few years old when I

17

began to ask questions such as 'Why was I born?' and I do recall that mother and father's answers did not satisfy me. That question actually remained unanswered until I reached about ten years old, when an Inner experience happened that set me firmly on the Path I have since traveled for many, many decades. I will tell you what happened that day...

"My parents, being sharecroppers in the deep South, had very little education and were hard put to answer the many questions I had about God and the universe. 'What is God?' I used to ask... 'Who am I to God?' 'What am I going to do with my life?' 'Where am I going?' 'Is God above me in the sky?' 'Does He hear me when I pray?'..... questions, Little One! I had so many questions!

"I knew that I wanted to learn to read and to write - to read the books of the world - to have knowledge open to me - to have a real teacher who could answer my questions! I wanted this so badly that many nights I found myself crying in my small room on the straw bed until, in the darkness, I fell asleep. When I was about ten years old, I began to have unusual dreams... dreams which I now understand, but at the time, because I had no reference points for what I felt to be very real occurrences, I awoke in the middle of the night with even more questions! There was never any

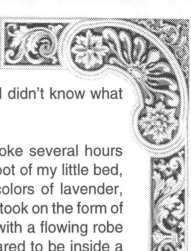

fear - just concern, because I didn't know what was happening to me.

"One such night, I awoke several hours before dawn. There, at the foot of my little bed, appeared a shining Light... colors of lavender, white and purple. It gradually took on the form of a beautiful, translucent man with a flowing robe and long dark hair that appeared to be inside a wrapped white turban. Blazing on his chest was an embroidered symbol which emitted a fiery Golden Light. I was sitting up in bed by this time and, oh, Little One, there was such a wave of Peace and Love coming from this Being that I did not know any fear. I heard his voice Inside me... his lips did not move. This seemed perfectly natural to me at the time. His words were very clear and they set the entire course of my lifetime. This is what he said to me in my heart..."

"Be not afraid, my child. I am he who has watched over you many lifetimes... have helped and guided you... have impressed you with great teachings. You are the most precious being in the world to me, for as you grow, so, too, do I. Your questions have certainly been heard. They have resounded across the universe, for, to the Father, no thought is lost... no thought is too small or too large to be answered. Know this well, Anelleh; that Force which mankind calls "God" is all around you! It is within all living things... every plant, every rock, every drop of water, every atom of air,

19

every bit of earth! It is within every bird, fish, animal - but most importantly, that Force which we call "God" is within every human being! Anelleh, you do not have to look anywhere for God except Inside yourself!"

"He had heard my unspoken thought of HOW can I find the God within me! How do I start? Who do I ask? With a warm, compassionate smile, this magnificent soul responded..."

"My child, you need only to close your eyes and still your thoughts. The Light you see Inside will take you to the Inner Areas of Thought, for God is also Pure Thought! Think on these things for a few days. I will return in the same manner three mornings hence and we will discuss what you have discovered Inside yourself."

"With these comments, this Being of Light faded and the room was as it was before his arrival. I laid back on my pillow, thinking hard of what had transpired. Then I drifted off into deep sleep until my mother awakened me a few hours later for the chores of the day."

Anelleh paused for a while, as was her practice. She wanted me to absorb what she was saying and also gave me time to write everything down as best I could in the notebook I always carried when visiting her. I enjoyed these moments too, as it created beautiful feelings between us

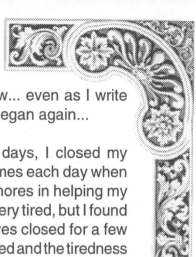

that I can still feel... right now... even as I write these words for you... She began again...

"During the next few days, I closed my eyes as instructed, several times each day when I had the time. Usually my chores in helping my parents always left me very, very tired, but I found that when I rested with my eyes closed for a few minutes I became very refreshed and the tiredness began to depart from me. I did indeed see interesting Lights inside my head. I didn't know where they came from, but I did know they were there! Sometimes the Lights were splashes, sometimes geometric shapes... sometimes they beckoned to me to go right through them...and one time I did!

"In my mind, I hurled my body through one of the beautiful pale blue Lights and found myself in an opulent garden! I saw and smelled roses... I had never seen so many roses! Pink... white... red! All in perfect bloom! I thought I could even touch them as well as enjoying their fragrance. I then felt myself walking around the garden and seated myself on what seemed to be a comfortable rock formation. Then, Little One, through this very same garden came the Being I saw in my room two nights earlier!

"The Light that shone from his countenance was almost more than I could bear... but even in this Inner Consciousness state, I was at peace.

He began to speak to me through thought, saying that I had followed his instructions very well and that, because of this, I would have more responsibilities added unto me. He indicated that within a few hours I would be approached by one of the school teachers in my town and that, as a result of this meeting, my parents would consent to have me study reading and writing during the afternoons. Thus another of my prayers was answered! I would truly be able to read and write... with this thought, the Being arose and left the garden. I opened my eyes, gradually, with a feeling of well-being all around me.

"Within about three hours my parents were visited by one of the school teachers in town, and the very next day I was in school! I learned very quickly, for I had the Inner feeling that I was being prepared for something... but I did not know what it was. I JUST KNEW. The next night I went to bed, praying in my heart that I would see the glorious man again, and it was so. I was gently awakened a few hours before dawn by the Being. This time he addressed himself to me in the following manner..."

"Salaam Alekum, Anelleh. May Peace be ever with you. You have done well and I am pleased."

"Who are you... what is your name?... again, Little One, all I had were questions!"

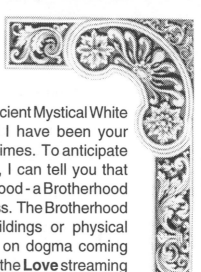

"My name within the Ancient Mystical White Brotherhood is Allahba and I have been your spiritual teacher for many lifetimes. To anticipate further questions, dear child, I can tell you that you are a part of that Brotherhood - a Brotherhood which is birthless and deathless. The Brotherhood does not have physical buildings or physical churches. It is not founded on dogma coming from the mind of man but from the **Love** streaming forth from that Force we call "God". Indeed, its power and authority comes from that Force - that Pure Essence which created all that is visible and invisible. Within The Ancient Mystical White Brotherhood is the Ancient Order of Melchizedek which means in the old Hebrew language, 'The Right Use of Higher Consciousness'.

"Members of this Brotherhood are many and are invisible to the eye of man. They represent every planet in our universe and beyond and the Highest Ones are called our Elder Brothers. We always work as **One**; never in competition. Those who have risen to the Order of Melchizedek are referred to as 'Sons of God'... Co-Creators. My child, there is no end to learning and no end to the limitless Light of Truth and Love. You are about to take your place, again, consciously in your physical body, in the workings of the Brotherhood on the Earthian plane.

"You, dear Anelleh, are awakening to your mission on this Earth. You will not see me physically for several Earth years, but you can always seek me Within yourself as you did yesterday in your garden. We shall speak of many things when you seek me Within.

"Salaam Alekum, dear Anelleh,... Salaam..."

"Little One, although I was only a young girl, I understood everything he said to me. It was a good five years later that I saw Allahba again, physically. I felt him around me and saw him in my Inner garden. Indeed, we did speak of many things. He told me I would be traveling the world over... to be placed into the hands of very great and wise teachers of the Brotherhood for specific lengths of time... to have my Inner centers awakened... to live the span of three lifetimes in one, and to pass on orally what I had learned and where I had traveled, to one soul who would give it to those who would listen... That soul is you, Little One, you!

"When I saw Allahba again, it was he who asked the questions...

"Salaam Alekum, Anelleh. Peace be ever with you. You have learned those concepts that the world can teach you. Do you now wish to

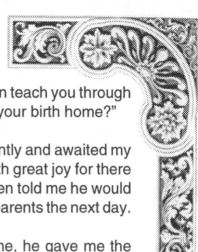

learn what your Inner Self can teach you through travel and learning far from your birth home?"

"He looked at me intently and awaited my answer. My heart leaped with great joy for there was YES in my heart! He then told me he would arrange everything with my parents the next day.

"Then, for the first time, he gave me the Sign with his hands. This was the outward signal of the Brotherhood... a Sign which I was to see throughout my travels the world over.

"The next day an unexpected letter arrived at our modest home. An anonymous donor had bequeathed a large sum of money to my parents to do with as they pleased and informed them that, with their permission and mine, the donor would give me further education in his city, treating me as a beloved daughter, giving me excellent tutelage. If this was agreeable, they were to speak with his emissary who would be at their home the following day and would answer all of their questions. Within two months I would be called for by the same emissary and taken to the large city.

"Little One, my parents loved me very, very much. They had a very difficult decision to make and after they had talked for a long time, they asked me my thoughts. It was a sad as well as a joyous moment for us all... you see, I was a child of their old age and I probably would not see them again for a long time. They knew this too, but they loved me so much; enough to let me go - to learn - to grow. The emissary came the following day as promised, and my parents gave their permission after speaking at length with the man.

"Within two months the same emissary arrived in a sturdy, handsome carriage for me. I remember the sadness on my parents faces and the silent tears they shed when I actually left. Indeed, it was the very last time I did see them physically, but I knew they were now cared for and would never toil physically again.

"With sadness on one side of me and a world of adventure on the other, I left with this ambassador of the Brotherhood. I believe I remember his name... Aaron. Yes, it was Aaron. A very loving man, about the same age as my father. I recall that he spoke with my parents to calm their hearts and minds that day. Indeed, Aaron treated me as his own daughter and showed me every kindness during the long journey to New York. During my travels over the next several decades, I met several Brothers with the name Aaron, all of different ages but all perfect examples of the training of the Brotherhood.

"We traveled several weeks by carriage before reaching New York City. I had never seen

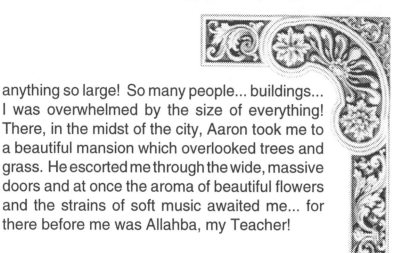

anything so large! So many people... buildings... I was overwhelmed by the size of everything! There, in the midst of the city, Aaron took me to a beautiful mansion which overlooked trees and grass. He escorted me through the wide, massive doors and at once the aroma of beautiful flowers and the strains of soft music awaited me... for there before me was Allahba, my Teacher!

"Words are inadequate to tell you how I felt at that moment! I couldn't get any words out of my throat! All my dear Teacher said to me was,"

"Salaam Alekum, Anelleh. May Peace be ever with you. Refresh yourself now. We will meet again later."

"With these words he slowly vanished from my sight! A beautiful woman entered the room where Aaron and I stood. He introduced her to me as his spiritual Sister, Rebecca. I was placed in her care and was taken to a quiet room wherein a robe was supplied for me to wear after I had bathed. Do you remember, Little One, that in each story I told you, wherever I went I was always expected to bathe myself and don the robes of the Order? It was so now. The countries I visited were all different, but the rites and preparations of the Order were all very similar.

"After the evening meal of fresh fruits, cheese and black bread, I was escorted into a large room at the very top of the building. There were no partitions in this large expanse of space... the carpeting was a very soft, very pale blue color. The furnishing around the sides of this chamber were also pale blue with gold accents. In the middle of the room was a triangular altar, surrounded by three tall, ornate candlesticks at right angles. The candles were lighted. On the opposite wall from where I stood was the emblem of the Order in gold... the same symbol I have seen in every Inner Temple I have ever had the privilege of entering and learning in. The wall I was facing was East.

"Within moments every chair around this chamber was filled with men and women representing every race and religion - every age and, I am sure, every social status. All were equal in this chamber. Then, materializing beside me, was Allahba.

"We approached the altar together at the middle of the room. An exquisite consciousness came over me as I approached the Sacred Triangle and knelt before it, facing the Symbol of the Brotherhood on the far wall.

"In that moment, Little One, as if I truly knew what was going to happen - what I was going to say - and to whom - I had the KNOWING THAT I HAD DONE THIS MANY TIMES BEFORE IN PAST LIVES! My Inner Awareness was being

28

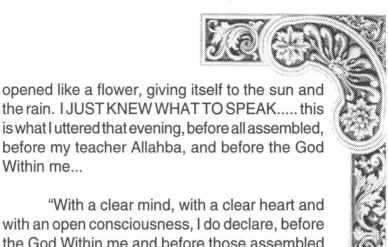

opened like a flower, giving itself to the sun and the rain. I JUST KNEW WHAT TO SPEAK..... this is what I uttered that evening, before all assembled, before my teacher Allahba, and before the God Within me...

"With a clear mind, with a clear heart and with an open consciousness, I do declare, before the God Within me and before those assembled in this chamber, that I assume the responsibilities of 'Neophyte' within The Ancient Mystical White Brotherhood. I will ever strive to learn and to grow and to place into practice the Great Universal Laws I have been and will be taught, so that my life is a teaching by example and that the Love Within my heart will shine as a beacon to all those who are searching for the Ancient Wisdoms. I also affirm that I will keep secret what I have learned and will learn until such time as I am permitted to disseminate this knowledge and wisdom. These concepts do I so affirm. In this manner I will know the age-old Truth, 'MAN, KNOW THYSELF'. So Mote It Be.

"Within the silence that followed was a celestial music too subtle for description. All within the room heard it, for it came from the hearts of all assembled. That was the source of the tones heard that day! Beautiful... truly beautiful! The words I heard in the music were..... FIAT LUX! LET THERE BE LIGHT!

"The three candles at the center altar glowed with more than a physical manifestation of Light... as if they were responding to my words and thoughts.

"When that moment passed, I was told by Allahba that my life was to be one of travel to many distant countries - to learn of the Ancient Wisdoms from their Temples - that I would be cared for in every way but that it was my responsibility to absorb as much as possible in preparation for the time I would disseminate it all to one person, with a clear memory on my part... who, in turn, would quietly tell these stories of my life to those who, someday, would also come to the Brotherhood in various ways. He told me in front of those assembled that my life span would exceed two hundred earth years and that when it was time for me to leave, I would have the ability to 'translate' into another dimension of life. He then asked if I was ready for these responsibilities, and I replied that I was.

"Little One, all this happened when I was only fifteen years old. But everything said in that chamber - so long ago - has come to pass. You are the one who will speak of my life, not to have people think I am a great teacher... no... but that I had learned to be a good student and that I TRIED!

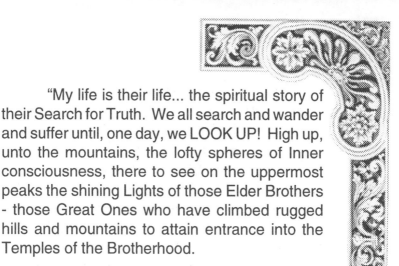

"My life is their life... the spiritual story of their Search for Truth. We all search and wander and suffer until, one day, we LOOK UP! High up, unto the mountains, the lofty spheres of Inner consciousness, there to see on the uppermost peaks the shining Lights of those Elder Brothers - those Great Ones who have climbed rugged hills and mountains to attain entrance into the Temples of the Brotherhood.

"The Path up to those peaks is very, very narrow and the higher we climb the rougher it becomes. So it is with those who enter upon the Path of the Ancient Ones, for the only way up is to LIVE THE TRUTH OF LOVE!

"You will then know the majesty of the Dance Within You, my Little One..."

As Anelleh said these words, she beckoned me towards her and placed her old hands upon my head as in a benediction. She said to me...

"Let the Light come to you and surround you with Heavenly White Fire! Claim the roses, sent from beyond the dawn of Time... dwell Within that Light, Little One. The secrets are buried very deeply Within you. Let your heart be opened. Let your mind be opened. The Great Ones are waiting for your Awakening!"

She gently took her hands from my head and settled back on her pillowed chair. I could not lift my eyes from her face... tears were coming down my cheeks. She had touched my very heart and soul... as we have touched each other this moment in my writing these words to you. Her story IS our story, my story, the story of our individual Search for that Force we call God. Truly, the Great Elder Brothers are waiting, waiting very deep Within us to show us the Ancient Paths to Portals we entered so long ago...

Perhaps we will sit once again, you and I, to speak of my beloved Teacher Anelleh and her unusual travels with the Brotherhood... Salaam Alekum... may Peace descend upon your soul this day...

The Chevron

and

The Crystal Ruby

Rose Pendant

*M*an has held caves in deep fascination throughout the dawning of Time. The feeling of warmth and security was comforting. There are many caves throughout the planet where advanced civilizations have hidden their secrets and their treasures. Anelleh imparted to me strange tales of such caves, some of them she said she had been taken to during her long years of study with the Great White Brotherhood. I remember well... it was during my fifth year with her. She called me to her beautiful, colorful garden. It was during the autumn season and the leaves that had fallen on the lawn began to dance while being caught up by friendly, warm breezes. Altogether it was a restful and quiet situation, conducive to her teachings...

Full of expectancy, I sat to her right and, with pen and tablet in hand, I was prepared to write what she spoke. I will tell you the story heard that day...

After making herself comfortable in an old wicker chair, Anelleh began to close her eyes, as she often did when she was recounting her adventures. It seemed to me that when she recalled an event, she would be mentally reliving it and actually going back in Time to recall everything as if it were all happening again. Knowing Anelleh's powers, she probably did live it again, just as fervently as when it happened the first time...

She began... "Little One, I told you before that in my travels around and in this planet so many years ago, I was guided by the invisible hand of The Ancient Mystical White Brotherhood. Guided as I was from master teacher to master teacher, I was always expected when I arrived at my destination.

"When I was about fifty years old, I was mentally instructed to travel to Peru. That was a difficult journey at that time, as all travel to South America was by boat and it took several months to make the trip. Having learned that I was cared for in every manner when the Brotherhood called, my faith was sufficient and I didn't ask WHY I was to go... I just went because I KNEW I would be instructed further into the Ancient Wisdoms.

"To the common person, I was a fool. My small savings were spent on this trip and I truly did not know where or what I was to do when the ship

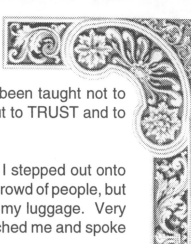

docked in Peru. But I have been taught not to think as the masses think, but to TRUST and to obey the Inner urgings.

"The ship docked and I stepped out onto the pier. I wasn't used to the crowd of people, but I waited patiently as I sat on my luggage. Very shortly a stately man approached me and spoke in impeccable English."

"Welcome, Anelleh. I trust that your voyage was pleasant. You will soon be able to refresh yourself. If you will be kind enough to come with me, my carriage will take you to a comfortable house where we will assist you in preparing for your journey to the high Andes Mountains."

"His eyes were kind and I instinctively trusted him. In appearance he looked without specific age but there was a nobility about him. This nobility was noticeable with each of the adepts I was privileged to study with over the years... wearing a deep blue cape, after the European style of the day, he gently led me to his waiting carriage. After we were settled, my guide smiled and said,"

"Call me Dr. Isa, Anelleh. It was a name given to me long years ago by Those whom we both Serve. It will be my responsibility to assist you with your orientation of this country during the next few weeks. A special diet has been prepared for you utilizing the good, ripe fruit of this country, soured milk and honey. With these foods in your body you will be cleansed during this short time for the experiences to come, which will be most important."

Anelleh stopped for a while and there actually seemed to be a hush in the wind around us. The leaves no longer danced and not even a bird sang. Although it lasted but a few moments, Anelleh was very sensitive to this stillness. I was very surprised at her next statement after the hush had passed...

"I was told long ago that there was such an entity known as The King of the World, who had his abode in the mystical city of Shamballah, deep within our planet. When the King of the World speaks, that vibration is so beautiful and powerful that it is felt by the surface animals and birds because of their sensitivity and attunement. When the vibration begins, a hush is felt and all of Nature becomes still to listen. Just such a moment has happened to us, and I stopped to listen too."

Looking over at me and seeing the expression of wonder on my face, she smiled and gave my arm a few pats, knowing that without the direct experience of what she was saying, it was difficult to grasp the Truths... sometimes uttered in parable. In due time, her story began again...

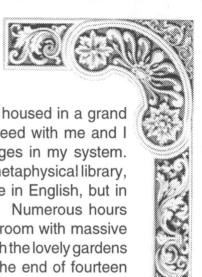

"For two weeks I was housed in a grand home in Lima. The diet agreed with me and I gradually saw positive changes in my system. The home had an extensive metaphysical library, many volumes of which were in English, but in many other languages also. Numerous hours were spent within that great room with massive texts as well as strolling through the lovely gardens surrounding the house. At the end of fourteen days, Dr. Isa returned for me. I was told not to bring any additional clothing; only my crystal pendant. The same carriage was to speed Dr. Isa and myself over the Peruvian landscape for several days, past Cusco, high into the Andes. When all traces of good road ended and our carriage could travel no further over the rocks, Dr. Isa dismissed the carriage and driver with appreciation and guided me by foot around a large mountain. This additional journey was five days in duration but our energy seemed limitless, even though the oxygen in the air was thin. We journeyed until we came to a large lake. This surprised me because it had not occurred to me that there could be such a lake so many thousands of feet above sea level. I noticed that there was a small population of native Indians living around the lake. As we approached them they were very cordial and seemed to definitely recognize Dr. Isa. The language spoken was not Spanish and Dr. Isa's command of the conversations was excellent and quite spirited!

"We waited only about an hour until a messenger arrived. He was wearing a smooth cream colored linen tunic which looked comfortable. Lowering their heads with respect to Dr. Isa, they exchanged verbal and hand sign greetings, after which I was introduced. With great cordiality, the messenger introduced himself simply as Aaron. He informed me that he was born and raised in England until maturity. His search for the Ancient Wisdoms was very powerful and, in due time, he was approached by an unusual man who began to instruct him. Approximately ten years ago he was given the opportunity to travel from England to this country to intensify the work begun in England.

I thought about this conversation as the three of us continued our journey an additional four miles due East, where we came to an unusually arched, carved stone doorway which had been chiseled from living rock. Along the sides of the arch were cryptic symbols akin to those I saw beneath the mountain in California when I was a younger woman. Although I could see through to the other side of the doorway and viewed a magnificent valley surrounded by the Andes mountains, the space between the arches was wavy - as if there was a force field which originated from the symbols that were carved on both sides of the arch.

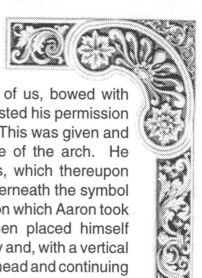

"Aaron stood in front of us, bowed with respect to Dr. Isa, and requested his permission to open the passage for us. This was given and Aaron went to the right side of the arch. He touched one of the symbols, which thereupon turned a vivid sky blue. Underneath the symbol there slid out a golden chevron which Aaron took into his right hand. He then placed himself directly in front of the archway and, with a vertical motion, beginning above his head and continuing down to his feet, the portal opened for us with a beautiful, musical sound. The wavy force field ceased. When we had passed to the other side, Aaron sealed the opening as he had opened it and replaced the chevron in its position so it could be utilized by the next person.

"It was explained to me by Dr. Isa that protecting all of the entrance ways to the secret places on our planet were vibrational fields set there long ago by the Old Ones. Such a sacred place was this community of the Brotherhood and to which we belonged. As we walked, Dr. Isa explained how the community began many thousands of years ago, by our Brothers from another planet within our solar system. Coming to Earth, they sought to teach the sacred sciences to mankind, which was developing beautifully on the now submerged continent called Lemuria. Realizing that the teachings had advanced as far as possible with the populace and knowing that the continent was soon to be submerged by the explosion of gases from deep within the ground, the Old Ones gathered those who had learned their teachings well and, on a date to remember, just moments prior to the deluge caused by exploding gases, the great lighter-than-air-ships of the Old Ones lifted gently and noiselessly from Lemuria, with the elect.

"Within moments, the final belches and moans of the continent took place and Lemuria went down beneath the waves as they looked on. Within a short time, the great ships landed at the valley you now see before you and the Brotherhood began again under the eldest of the Old Ones. Even at that time he was considered old, as we calculate time, for he had and still has learned the process by which the body rejuvenates itself continually.

"Many of the Old Ones have passed from our community since that time, as they had felt that their Service was needed more elsewhere. But, the eldest is still amongst us.

"Little One, I was enthralled with what I saw! The beauty of unusual trees, flowers - but the most beautiful feeling was from the people who greeted me as one of their own. There were Neophytes and Initiates from all over the world, representing every race and language. The roles of men and women were equal to provide the balance of life in all things. Dr. Isa and Aaron led

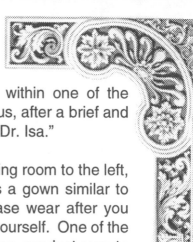

me to a beautiful chamber within one of the mountains. Here Aaron left us, after a brief and respectful conversation with Dr. Isa."

"You will find a changing room to the left, Anelleh. Within the room is a gown similar to Aaron's, which you will please wear after you have bathed and refreshed yourself. One of the Sisters of our Order will then conduct you to where I will be when all is in readiness."

"The bathing water had the aroma of sandalwood and was unusually soothing after our journey. When I was ready to be conducted to Dr. Isa, a young woman came for me. She seemed to be about twenty-five years old. However, when I spoke to her, she remarked that she had recently passed her seventy-fifth birthday! Smiling at my look of surprise, she commented, 'Anelleh, when students learn very diligently and their love for the Ancient Wisdoms becomes an integral part of their lives, the knowledge doesn't stay in the mind. The knowledge is integrated into our lives every day. We are taught that the body is so constructed that there is no reason for the organs to decay, atrophy or become diseased. It is only when thoughts - known to the outer world as hatred, envy, jealousy, greed, suspicion and lying come into our lives that our bodies begin to age. Our thoughts govern universes, including the universe of our body! The ancient teaching, 'As Above, So Below' is very valid, for as the universes are governed with Love and serve us for millions of years with sustaining materials, so our bodies can serve us for many hundreds, thousands and, in the case of the Old One who is the head of our Brotherhood, several millions of years. When travel in the human vehicle is no longer desirable for the Service that we are performing, we can consciously lay that vehicle aside to return to the elements, whereupon we ascend to a Higher level of Service in a lighter body which we have earned the right to magnetize to ourselves. I came here from Egypt, Anelleh, as a young woman of twenty-four years. I am told I look no older now than the first day I entered the portal."

"We walked through the passageways carved in the living rock, just below the surface of the earth. I was led to Dr. Isa who had also changed his garment to a violet linen robe. There was a gold and purple insignia above his right breast which was the sacred symbol of the Brotherhood. My guide gave a respectful look to Dr. Isa, exchanging a sign with her right hand. She then departed, leaving Dr. Isa and I alone in the room."

"Anelleh, I trust you are well rested. Please, seat yourself."

"When we had settled ourselves in the large and very comfortable chairs in the chamber,

44

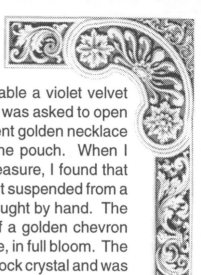

Dr. Isa took from a nearby table a violet velvet pouch and handed it to me. I was asked to open it and, when I did, a magnificent golden necklace was lying at the bottom of the pouch. When I reached in to take out the treasure, I found that there was an unusual pendant suspended from a golden chain, which was wrought by hand. The pendant was in the shape of a golden chevron upon which was carved a rose, in full bloom. The rose was chiseled from pure rock crystal and was perfect in every way. Touching it was an extraordinary experience... it emitted waves of Peace, Peace, Peace ..."

"Wear this pendant during your seven year sojourn with us, Anelleh. It will not only serve to admit you to many areas of our school and libraries, but will serve to keep your physical, mental and spiritual bodies in perfect harmony. You will also find that it emits a very pleasing tone once in a while. As it becomes more and more frequent, you will know that your progress with us is accelerating. The tone you will hear will actually be coming from your very Soul. The pendant will only be acting as a receiver to that transmission."

"Placing it around my neck as I arose was a moment to cherish. During my years there, the necklace never left me and I did indeed hear the music from my deepest Soul. I learned from this that each of us has a tone which is a harmonic from our Soul and that it can be heard, even without such a receiver as the chevron and the crystal ruby rose.

"Little One, there are a few teachings and experiences that I am not permitted at this time to impart to you regarding my time spent in this Inner School, but there are a few I can impart. I will tell you of just one of these experiences now...

"Dr. Isa taught me very often during those seven years... the secret doctrines of lost civilizations were learned from ancient scrolls whose languages I was able to decipher with the crystal pendant given me by Auuran at San Jacinto Mountain years ago... and which I keep on my person continually. But the most fascinating way of all to learn is by time travel to the specific ancient civilization! I cannot tell you too much, but I can say that there is a very large golden disc which is suspended from golden cords in one of the larger chambers within the complex. After I was taught by Dr. Isa to be proficient in thinking one thought only, he conducted me to the room with the disc. This disc was very sensitively attuned to thought frequencies and vibrations and therefore one's thoughts must be very pure. Dr. Isa stood to the left of the disk and told me to touch his right shoulder with my left hand... thereupon to think single-pointedly of a specific destination and point in time agreed to beforehand. The first time this was done, we traveled back in time to ancient Greece during the lifetime of

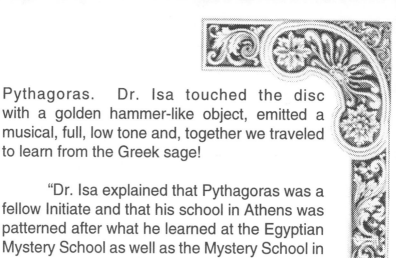

Pythagoras. Dr. Isa touched the disc with a golden hammer-like object, emitted a musical, full, low tone and, together we traveled to learn from the Greek sage!

"Dr. Isa explained that Pythagoras was a fellow Initiate and that his school in Athens was patterned after what he learned at the Egyptian Mystery School as well as the Mystery School in Athens. You see, Little One, this rare opportunity was given to me not only to read the actual ancient scrolls that Pythagoras wrote personally, but to learn from him in person... this was more than I ever dreamed was possible! I will definitely say that it seemed to me that Pythagoras knew Dr. Isa, as there was never a question from the sage when we attended lectures in his round classrooms... only a smile of acknowledgment from the sage to Dr. Isa.

"I was also to learn that this disc transported Initiates from one part of the planet to the other and back again during our own time period. In this way physical communication was always possible in the third dimension.

"Returning to our time period from the school in Athens was a little more difficult than getting there. We stood on exactly the same spot as we did when we materialized at the Athenian School. Then, with single-pointed thought, placing within our minds the picture of the room in which the golden disc hung, Dr. Isa emitted the same tone and we were once again in the great chamber. I realized that the tone is so important because the disc vibrated exactly the same tone as Dr. Isa emitted, which brought us back along the same vibrational wave length. The Laws are very simple. However, their understanding and application may take lifetimes!

"Knowing that my seven years were almost completed at that location of the Brotherhood's schools, and that I would be returning to the outer world again, still there was a realization that many tests of life were passed and that I had entered the Brotherhood on a permanent basis, at the age of fifty-seven. My thoughts communicated this to Dr. Isa and he confirmed this Truth. The beautiful chevron and ruby rose pendant was returned with grateful appreciation. But, Little One, I feel I am wearing it still... for its imprint in the Akasha is still vibrating... and the tone still sings in my heart!"

As my beloved teacher Anelleh spoke, small tears came to her face... a face now beginning to show signs of aging, but yet so sensitive and beautiful to me. Yes, Anelleh's soul sang with a beauty of many hearts in accord, but the song was never so powerful as when she taught me... trusting that I would someday pen her story after she returned, in spirit, to those Old Ones who taught her so well.

The song of trust - of love that a teacher has for a student... that is the music I heard that day!

Perhaps we will sit again, you and I, another time and place, and I will tell you other journeys my beloved teacher Anelleh told me, of her adventures in forgotten places...

The

Temple

of

The

Living

Light

*I*n two words, Anelleh shared a philosophy "Experience living!" She used to say to me...

"Little One, the books of the world, however brilliantly worded, can teach the intellect only. To really learn, one must be able to think! Thinking is very simple, yet so many complicate the process! Experience living, forming high codes of behavior that will lead to future Awareness. Remember, an aware person depends upon Inner Strength and Experience as the greatest book!"

What comes to mind at this time is an unusual experience she told me several years ago. Each time I read her words, it's like being there with her... One day she related this story to me... it begins like this, in her words...

"Little One, long ago when I was about twenty-five years into my spiritual disciplines with the Brotherhood, I received a letter in quite an unconventional manner. While I was reading in my room, a letter appeared on the table near my hand. This had happened to me before and I began to realize that this was one of the ways in which the Adepts communicated with their chelas around the world. My name was beautifully inscribed on this unusual letter in delicate lettering. As usual it was sealed with a violet wax imprint of the Order.

"I opened the envelope and recognized the writing of my Teacher, instructing me to travel to Greece within the month and that all arrangements would be handled properly. I remember the excitement welling up inside me as I began to make preparations, knowing that the Master would have all in readiness for me when the time came to board the large sailing vessel... and it was so.

"The trip was long but peaceful... after changing ships twice, I finally saw the magnificent blue of the Aegean Sea, dotted by so many mountainous islands. The ship had to travel carefully around these islands until I arrived in Athens. I was met by one of the Brothers who escorted me to a home maintained by the Order in the city, there to refresh myself and rest for several days. The Brother's name was Anaxagoras, after the great Greek philosopher who lived around 500 B.C. This gentle Brother was very correctly named, for, like his ancient

54

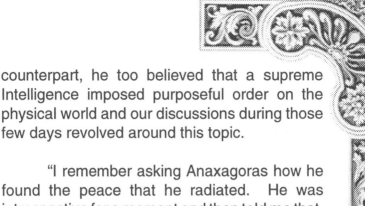

counterpart, he too believed that a supreme Intelligence imposed purposeful order on the physical world and our discussions during those few days revolved around this topic.

"I remember asking Anaxagoras how he found the peace that he radiated. He was introspective for a moment and then told me that, several decades ago, he had made a considerable fortune in the market places of the world. However, he was rarely at peace with himself... never really content with his life. The religion into which he was born did not give him the answers to the fluid questions which flowed never-ending from his mind. His family was growing away from him, and, in his quiet moments, the loneliness screamed all around him... the feeling of not having anyone with whom to discuss the thoughts he had... he thought his only attribute for mankind was knowing how to make more and more money. After his children had attained to maturity, his wife died and he left his business in capable hands. He then traveled the world, learning personally how people lived and coped with their everyday problems of living. He always helped them when he could. After about three years of traveling, he was approached by one of the older Brothers of the Order while staying in Paris. He said this was about fifteen years ago. Although he was now seventy-two years old, he appeared to be no older than about forty-five. The substance of what he told me was that, by living the philosophies he learned, changes came about within him. His spiritual Work for the Order now makes him an emissary for their work throughout the world and his learning continues by direct experience each day.

"There was a peacefulness about him that made me feel very secure and loved... as if this man was the father that I knew so long ago but who had passed on to a Higher reality.

"After I rested sufficiently, Anaxagoras took me to the Parthenon. Even though it was in a partial state of ruin, still its majesty spoke boldly. I marveled that such a building, constructed over 2,400 years ago - used for the first nine hundred years by the Greeks as a Temple to Athena - then for nearly one thousand years after that as a Christian Church - then for two hundred years as a Moslem mosque... has endured the ravages of Man and Nature. As this dear man spoke to me of these pages in the Parthenon's history, I became interested in going to the inside court of the building. As we walked around this court, with the sun shining into parts of the edifice, Anaxagoras spoke quietly to me, saying,

"Anelleh, you are walking where once there was a giant statue to the goddess Athena, fashioned of the purest gold and ivory, around a wooden core crafted by the master artisan Phidias. It was Pallas Athena who was born, fully grown,

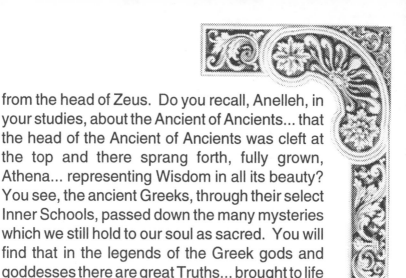

from the head of Zeus. Do you recall, Anelleh, in your studies, about the Ancient of Ancients... that the head of the Ancient of Ancients was cleft at the top and there sprang forth, fully grown, Athena... representing Wisdom in all its beauty? You see, the ancient Greeks, through their select Inner Schools, passed down the many mysteries which we still hold to our soul as sacred. You will find that in the legends of the Greek gods and goddesses there are great Truths... brought to life by those who have Keys to the Mysteries."

Anelleh paused for a moment and, as was her usual way, she looked at me directly, not only to see if I was still interested in what she was saying, but it was as if she could look clear through me to see if I was **understanding** what she said. Satisfied, she again closed her eyes and continued...

"Anaxagoras and I sat down on one of the fallen pieces of stone outside the Parthenon. He then spoke to me again."

"Anelleh, you are to experience, in a direct physical manner, what few humans have experienced. Your travels and studies with teachers of our Order over the years has prepared you for this moment... look carefully around you... the hill where this Parthenon stands marks the site of yet another holy sanctuary... for below the Parthenon is another Temple, not dedicated to any ancient god or goddess, but to the Wisdom, Knowledge and Love Within Man which produces Light! This Temple has always been known by the name...

...The Temple of the Living Light."

"My delight at such an opportunity showed on my face, for there was a smile of acknowledgment from this soul. We descended the hill for a short distance, pausing in front of a large rock that was standing upright on one of the slopes. Anaxagoras stood before it, closed his eyes and emitted a high-pitched but soothing tone which was very peaceful. The rock began to move and, in a few seconds an opening large enough to admit us appeared. There was a well lit stairway before us and, as we took the first steps downward, the rock door closed behind us quickly. These were ancient stairs, cut into the living stone centuries before the Parthenon was built above us... smooth stairs, worn in the middle by the footsteps of those seeking Light for over three thousand years! The source of light on the steps making our way safe could not be found, but it was soft to my eyes and completely restful after the Athenian sunlight.

"After descending deeply within the hard stone, we reached an exquisite chamber. On the walls were painted realistic scenes of ancient Greek Initiation rites by men and women of

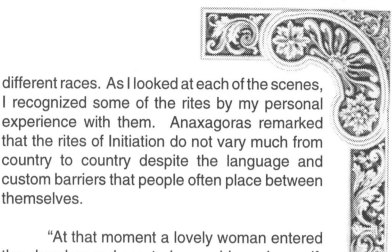

different races. As I looked at each of the scenes, I recognized some of the rites by my personal experience with them. Anaxagoras remarked that the rites of Initiation do not vary much from country to country despite the language and custom barriers that people often place between themselves.

"At that moment a lovely woman entered the chamber and greeted my guide and myself. Looking gently at me, she spoke in a wondrous voice."

"My name within our Order is Sappho, after the sixth century poet of this country. She, after whom I am named, was greatly admired for her lyrical style of writing. It has become an honor to carry on the vibration of her name."

"There was a genuine sweetness in her voice... much like the poetry of the woman whose name she bore..."

Anelleh became quiet again and very reflective. In consciousness she was reliving these meaningful moments and I have learned so much through these oral teachings, for they did not come solely from books but from her wealth of personal, direct experience... the finest teacher! She taught me not to rely solely on the words of others to live my life, but to have the courage to seek out and learn about living by living! To

59

accept what was felt to be Truth and to set aside that which was not... this was a great philosophy... to learn by experience! A slight smile was on her face as she continued her story...

"Anaxagoras placed me in Sappho's care, promising to see me again during my stay. As Sappho guided me through several corridors, we passed a few other men and women, all clothed in the traditional Grecian clothing even though they were of different races. Their Inward beauty was as food for my soul.

"I was led into what could be described as a clothing room... I was asked to bathe and reclothe myself in a robe similar to those we had passed in the corridor. When this was done, Sappho came for me and guided me through passageways into an extremely large chamber, seemingly hand carved from the rock. Again, light was present and I could not ascertain its source or where the consistent stream of fresh air - very cool and soothing air - came from. This air flowed freely throughout the Temple complex. As if reading my mind, Sappho began to speak..."

"The ancient members of our Order built into the very walls of this Inner Temple a substance which is activated by human thought... as long as the thought is present, so, too, is the light energy which is mirrored from the sun. The fresh air is constantly being filtered from the outside and

60

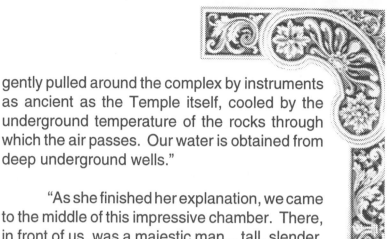

gently pulled around the complex by instruments as ancient as the Temple itself, cooled by the underground temperature of the rocks through which the air passes. Our water is obtained from deep underground wells."

"As she finished her explanation, we came to the middle of this impressive chamber. There, in front of us, was a majestic man... tall, slender, with a smooth face and long white hair. His face, however, did not show outward signs of aging. He began speaking..."

"My name is Callicrates. This Temple, and those within its walls, bid you welcome..."

"Little One, my soul, my very being tingled with a feeling that cannot be placed into words... this beautiful man gave out the energy of great Wisdom and Compassion. Looking into his eyes was like seeing everything I ever did and being totally understood, without judgment... of being accepted as someone very beautiful, even though men and women of Earth were rarely kind to me because of the dark complexion of my skin. Such Kindness came from his eyes... such Love...

"His long, white Grecian-style robe had small golden embroidery on the sleeves and at the hem of the garment and, embroidered upon the center of the garment on his chest, was the symbol of the Order. Although he did not say it,

I received the impression he was in charge of this Temple.

"He graciously motioned to me to be seated on one of the chairs provided and, when comfortable, Sappho retired from the room. Sitting with this man was like the peace one feels after opening one's eyes after deep meditation. Callicrates saw that I was comfortable. He began, in a few words, to teach me... I don't recall every word, but I was feeling more than he was saying... this is the essence of his teaching that day..."

"Anelleh, do not be what others expect you to be. You will only disappoint them as well as yourself. Be who you are, as you have earned the privilege to be taught by unusual and varied spiritual experiences over a long physical lifetime in association with our Brotherhood... an Order which you have associated yourself with in numerous lifetimes. In the decades to come, there will be attracted to you a person to whom you can impart your experiences and she, in turn, will place them in the printed word for others to read. This soul will also come to us for learning when the time is right.

"As you travel in the years ahead, remember that you will be learning from many people, representing many races. It is not **how** you were created that matters as much as **how well** you return yourself to God. The great

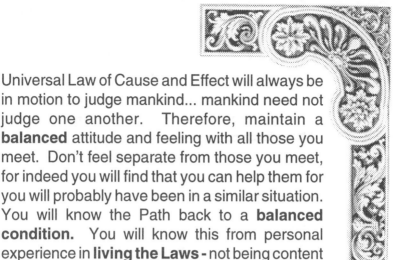

Universal Law of Cause and Effect will always be in motion to judge mankind... mankind need not judge one another. Therefore, maintain a **balanced** attitude and feeling with all those you meet. Don't feel separate from those you meet, for indeed you will find that you can help them for you will probably have been in a similar situation. You will know the Path back to a **balanced condition.** You will know this from personal experience in **living the Laws** - not being content to read the Laws. Remember too, that one's personal religion is not separate from any other religion... **for wherever there is a spark of life, there too is God, the Creator. Wherever God is, Therefore I AM.** We no longer look upon ourselves as totally separate but as part of a whole concept... a whole Infinite Intelligence whose vastness one can only begin to appreciate in a deep meditative experience when one sees **Great Light in a Sparkling Darkness.**

"In this state there is no breath, as one becomes the total Breath... one sees with a vision that is total... everywhere simultaneously... for in that moment, that instant, one can begin to experience God with a velvet touch upon the top of one's head that is transforming forever and never forgotten!

"When you begin to reach these experiences, each day will yet be another opportunity to dedicate yourself to very high principles and aspirations. There will always be those who will misunderstand you and perhaps bring you pain and suffering. **Bring the Light which you experience in deepest meditation to that situation and the pain will cease...** as pain produces shadows over the soul... **Light always dissipates the shadows!!**

"All of these concepts imply that we must love one another without conditions... for Love is the Essence of all Light and all Universal Law!"

"I don't remember Callicrates saying anything else verbally. He just closed his eyes and I did the same. The meditation experience that day was very profound... it was as if I had gone beyond the suns of all the solar systems and all the planets and entered other dimensions... the feeling of great humility as well as great power... both at the same time... surged through me. When I breathed, ALL UNIVERSES BREATHED and, through it all, the presence of Callicrates was beside me... and yet, he too was a part of me... can you comprehend what I'm telling you, Little One?"

I told her that without having the experience myself, I could only comprehend it intellectually... she said, "Some day you will, you will..."

She was quiet again, but gradually she continued her story...

64

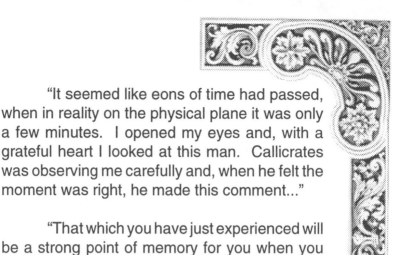

"It seemed like eons of time had passed, when in reality on the physical plane it was only a few minutes. I opened my eyes and, with a grateful heart I looked at this man. Callicrates was observing me carefully and, when he felt the moment was right, he made this comment..."

"That which you have just experienced will be a strong point of memory for you when you again commune with the Divine Intelligence. Through this experience, the supreme teacher, you can receive insights into any thought, concept or question... remember, **there is nothing new** in this or any other universe... **Everything that is, was!** All is contained within the heartbeat of the Eternal..."

"We rose and Sappho came into the room. Callicrates continued..."

"Stay with us as long as you feel learning takes place within you, Anelleh. Then your travels will begin again and we will place you in the hands of others."

"I had just opened my mouth to thank him when he slowly began to disappear from physical sight... only a vibrational energy remained where he once stood. The few words he spoke to me were profound and quite reflective. I thought about what he said for several years in my sojourn within the Temple of the Living Light. Many areas of the Temple were open to me, including the ancient library... the peace I knew there was soothing to my soul, intensified not only by the knowledge I obtained, but by each of the souls I met there.

"At the end of three years I was called again by Callicrates to the same large chamber. In the middle of the room appeared two columns. They looked as if they were chiseled from translucent marble. I could only assume that they were manifested there for a purpose I did not understand. Callicrates stood between these columns. The one to his right was of a golden color, beautifully fluted at the base with the ancient symbol of the Son/Sun of God carved on the front in addition to the other unusual cryptic symbols. This column was topped with a golden, glowing fire... not like the fire we understand that gives off heat... no... this was the fire of the legendary burning bush - consuming but not burning.

"The other column had the symbol of the Daughter of God carved on the front as well as other beautiful symbols. On top of this column was a small silver tree with nine branches and a sturdy trunk. Upon each leaf I could ascertain a Hebrew letter had been carved.

"Callicrates waited until my attention flowed back to him... and then he spoke, softly but with sureness..."

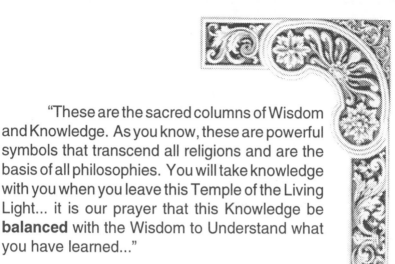

"These are the sacred columns of Wisdom and Knowledge. As you know, these are powerful symbols that transcend all religions and are the basis of all philosophies. You will take knowledge with you when you leave this Temple of the Living Light... it is our prayer that this Knowledge be **balanced** with the Wisdom to Understand what you have learned..."

"Thereupon he reached out his right arm towards the right column and, immediately appearing in the palm of his upturned hand was a tiny golden leaf from the Tree of Life."

"Into your heart I place this tiny flame of the Son/Sun of God - the principle of Knowledge and Creativity... and at the same time placing within your heart this little silver leaf from the Tree of Life, which is Wisdom. It represents all that is Intuitive and Temperate. The little leaf also holds the Hebrew letter Aleph which is a silent letter - a vowel - it means to keep all within your heart, being careful to whom you give the precious gems of hard-earned Knowledge and Wisdom."

"Both were passed into my heart and, within moments, the feeling of compassion, expectation and joy engulfed me... all I could do was just let the tears come softly...

"The columns faded slowly from the room. Callicrates remained and told me that my life's journey would be many fold and that others were available to teach me. I walked from the room with Sappho, who placed her arm around my shoulders and walked with me in silence out of the chamber.

"I rested for a few days, knowing my time within the Temple of the Living Light was near its end. I wanted to allow time for the experience to settle within my soul.

"Plans were made for my return to America. Sappho escorted me out of the Inner Temple by another way, which was shown to me a few years before... a way into Athens through a long, narrow corridor which ended in front of a large oak door, with a detailed symbol of the Brotherhood carved on it.

"We embraced at the door and I came into the fragrant garden I had entered on several occasions. One of the Brothers came for me and, after a brief meal I was given all that was necessary for my voyage home. In a few years I was again contacted by the same letter method and instructed to travel to Egypt... but that is another story... a story of the Temple at Sais...

"I must rest now, Little One... here, take these from my hand..."

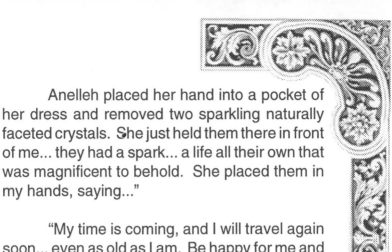

Anelleh placed her hand into a pocket of her dress and removed two sparkling naturally faceted crystals. She just held them there in front of me... they had a spark... a life all their own that was magnificent to behold. She placed them in my hands, saying..."

"My time is coming, and I will travel again soon... even as old as I am. Be happy for me and do not forget my words... these crystals are Keys to Ancient Portals... you will know exactly what to do with them when you need their energies. They are twins... having complimentary tones. Yes, you will HEAR the tones they sing in time! Take care of them... as they were placed in my care for my own use, so,too, do I pass them along to you... hold them to your heart, my child... remember what I have told you..."

How could I forget?....

Anelleh

and

the

Test

of

Gold

Understanding came to me in the fullness of time, for Anelleh's stories were so gentlein their teachings. The teaching, from mouth to ear, has always been the way of the great Masters.

It was about the third year of her instruction to me that the following tale was told... we were walking in a nicely shaded area when Anelleh pointed to a peaceful, grassy area which had strong, healthy trees. She began...

"In the teachings of the Ancient Wisdoms, we are tested before additional information is placed in our care. I was mentally impressed to travel to special places around the world, there to drink deeply of the Wisdom of the Initiates. There was an interesting experience in China... the Inner direction to me was to seek out the wise sage Chee-On-Lee in a particular province. He had just celebrated the 150th anniversary of his birth the afternoon I arrived. As always, when I studied with the sages, my arrival was anticipated and accommodations were in readiness.

"China has a deep repository of spiritual wealth and from Chee-On-Lee I learned much... to still my cravings for excess food, bodily and mental passions and, above all, I learned to cultivate patience, just as one cultivates a garden."

I noted a far away smile and it was some moments before Anelleh resumed her tale... when she did, she turned her face full at me, that face which showed little aging. She continued slowly...

"It was in a garden of beautiful flowers that I learned best from this sage. He asked that each motion of my hand and heart be smooth and unhurried... that my thinking during my gardening be lofty and filled with Love... and that I begin to innately understand the consciousness of the plants and flowers as they were growing. I remember one very warm summer afternoon. Sitting down to rest awhile, I picked a beautiful flower for Chee-On-Lee. While holding the flower in my hand, I felt my thoughts drifting away. At that moment, I wasn't 'me' anymore... my thoughts were flowing up and down the stem of the flower in my hand! I actually seemed to experience the flower and my life force became the same as the flower's. How long I was in this consciousness I can't say, but the feeling was at once odd and comfortable. It was then that I realized the Plant Kingdom has the same spark of life as is given to humans by our Creator, and that all Kingdoms of Life are Children of the Infinite Divine Life - God.

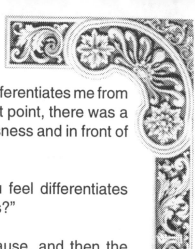

Then I asked myself, 'what differentiates me from the Plant Kingdom?' At that point, there was a return to my bodily consciousness and in front of me was Chee-On-Lee."

"Think! What do you feel differentiates Man from all other Kingdoms?"

"There was a long pause, and then the sage continued..."

"It is the power of thought, the power of reason and the ability to step up our evolution to grow and totally understand the pulse beat of that which we call God!"

"We studied in this manner for many years. The lessons learned, even for that point in my development, could not be rushed. Learning patience, tolerance, forbearance, understanding and stilling the mind is generally perfected over lifetimes. I was very fortunate to have such a teacher as Chee-On-Lee.

"Near the end of my study with this sage, on a day that will never be forgotten, this is what happened... I was studying in the teacher's library. He had taught me two ancient languages and had requested that I assist him in translating an old scroll that had been presented to him by his teacher a very long time ago. The contents of the scroll told of the civilization in China at the time of the great continent Atlantis. The writing was in pictographs but, once learned, the translation came quickly. The scroll's translation was almost complete at the time of this unusual occurrence. I remember being very engrossed in visualizing this ancient civilization which was far more advanced than we are today... when a letter manifested in front of me. It appeared on top of the scroll I was translating. The handwriting was flawless and the ink looked as if it had just dried. An unusual violet wax seal was at the top of the page - it looked as if it had been marked with a deeply grooved signet ring. This was not the first time such a communication was sent to me... the symbol in the wax was that of the Brotherhood.

"The letter, written in cipher, requested me to go into the meditation temple that evening prior to sunset. My teacher's temple was very small, but beautiful in its simplicity. Emanations of peace and tranquility flowed from it, invested, I'm sure, by many decades of devotional prayer and meditation.

"I arose and went to find the sage. Showing him the letter, which was not a surprise to him, he had a serious expression on his face. Without a word, he placed his right hand over my forehead, looked directly into my eyes, then slowly turned away, heading for his garden.

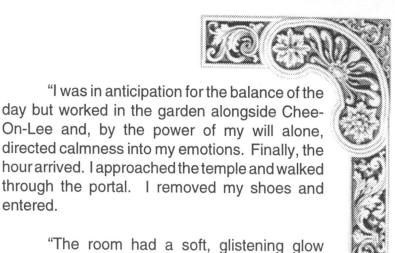

"I was in anticipation for the balance of the day but worked in the garden alongside Chee-On-Lee and, by the power of my will alone, directed calmness into my emotions. Finally, the hour arrived. I approached the temple and walked through the portal. I removed my shoes and entered.

"The room had a soft, glistening glow which was comfortable to my eyes. Standing in front of me were twelve men and women, dressed in loosely fitting pale lavender gowns, belted at the waist with long cords of golden material. I noticed that they represented all races, and the glow from them was loving and comforting. I was immediately set at rest.

"Directly in front of me there appeared a magnificent assortment of precious gems and golden nuggets. They glistened and sparkled and would certainly be worth many times a king's ransom. I felt overwhelmed at the sight of all this wealth!

"Then, I heard one of those assembled say to me..."

"Anelleh, all of this wealth you see before you is yours. If you accept it you will never have any apprehension about your material well-being in this lifetime. However, I am bidden to tell you that if you accept this wealth, you will live henceforth as any other human on this earth, living a normal lifespan, for the Karma of this wealth may weigh heavily upon you. You may choose with your free will, for the Love we have for you will transcend your decision this day."

"For a moment I will admit that I was tempted. But that was only for a moment... for all my training with Chee-On-Lee, whom I knew to be one of the Brotherhood, came flooding into my mind. I very quickly responded... 'My sustenance does not come from the gold and gems of this world - they are unreal. The only Reality is the Infinite Divine Life, God, and I strive to become One with that Source of all manifestation. The most beautiful flower in my garden needs not the jewels crafted by man to make it more beautiful. I cannot choose what is unreal. I choose the Higher Reality.'

"From someplace Within me, I heard the words..."

"You have chosen well..."

"The gems and gold, as well as the men and women I had just beheld all faded from physical view and I was now alone in the Temple. Staying there a while to contemplate what had just occurred, there was a realization that my understanding had increased but I still had questions. What was totally understood was the

peace I felt within myself, and that **I sincerely believed what I had said**. This was a feeling of wholeness and what I felt to be growth for my soul.

"It was late in the afternoon when I came from the Temple... only the glow of sunset remained to offset the darkness. Chee-On-Lee met me. He had a glowing expression on his face and blessed me as he had done that morning, saying,"

"Soon you will leave our garden and travel to another one who will guide you. From this servant of God you have learned all that is necessary at this point in your development. I am pleased..."

"There was a calmness Within him that flowed into my heart. I knew there would be sadness when I left him... this Brother who had the patience to teach that very quality...

"Little One, I realized at that point that, while Chee-On-Lee would never consider himself a lonely person, there were genuinely few people who were strong enough in their wisdom to practice their own teachings, even though they may be the only ones walking a different path. Time and again the teaching was given to me from many sources that there are very few who travel the Path to the Ancient Wisdoms... that Path being steep, narrow and strewn with difficulties that test, test and test yet again the Inner qualities of the aspirant. Such a soul was this sage. When he turned to walk away, his back was still erect, even at his advanced age... his health was excellent. Only his deep, liquid eyes told his story...

"Although I asked him several times about his life, he diverted my questions to my own studies. All he ever told me was that he was born into royalty in China and had every comfort in the physical. When he came to manhood, restlessness came over him. He indicated his life seemed to lack meaning and was devoid of function and purpose. He felt a great emptiness inside and his restlessness manifested in the desire to take his own life - amid the splendor of worldly possessions. He said this feeling built over several years. Just seconds before that moment came, a Great One, whom he now knows as one of the teachers of the Ancient Mystical White Brotherhood, appeared to him. That moment changed his life so completely, for the Brother began to teach him of the Universal Laws which govern all time and space - all dimensions of life, as well as mankind. He was taught the responsibility of all life, and that it is more courageous to live and to accept life's responsibilities than to disregard life. Gradually, the Light of Understanding flooded his soul. Taking leave of the palace, he left with the Brother and

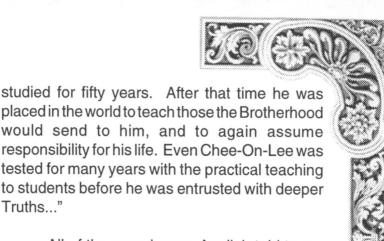

studied for fifty years. After that time he was placed in the world to teach those the Brotherhood would send to him, and to again assume responsibility for his life. Even Chee-On-Lee was tested for many years with the practical teaching to students before he was entrusted with deeper Truths..."

All of the experiences Anelleh told to me have been set down in writing. Her journeys in China, Tibet, Egypt, the Yucatan, the desolate areas of Persia... and more... were points of greater understanding for her after her unusual experiences when she was a young girl traveling in southern California. She told me she sometimes went back to San Jacinto Mountain, sometimes in her Light body and other times physically. She often said that the Ancient Mystical White Brotherhood had chelas worldwide. After so many stories by Anelleh, my belief became very strong with the prayer that one day I would walk in her footsteps. This has come to pass, little by little...

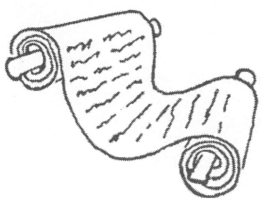

Anelleh

and

The Ancient Inner Earth

Civilization

*C*ould it have been so long ago since she and I spoke together? My memory of her still sparkles, even now, twenty-five years after her transition... my life has changed so much because of her.

People said that their parents, grandparents and as far back as anyone can remember, talked of old Anelleh. This is the last story that dear Anelleh told me. Perhaps it was the combination of where she told the story, as well as the story itself that caused the imprint to remain so long, for it was on her deathbed that this tale was related... she had asked me to come to her small home in the morning. I found her sitting up in bed... I even thought she told me she was preparing to enter a Higher Reality for sadness came over me. Sensing this, my hand was taken very lovingly and I sat down on the bed.

"Listen well, Little One. I'm going to tell you of another adventure. When you feel the time is right, begin to tell all of my stories as a teaching."

My head instinctively nodded but the tears came just the same. I placed my hands over my face for a short time because I knew the tears would be coming... this was unlike me, for all said that my emotions are not easily displayed. But I've always been at ease with this dear lady, and I felt no shame or guilt if I cried. I relaxed and composed myself, opening the briefcase which always accompanied me to Anelleh's house, and took out a large tablet. I was ready to listen, to observe and to record. These three things Anelleh taught me well.

She began, first looking at me as if she saw 'beyond' me... then, closing her eyes, she started to speak...

"In the old times, before there were many people on Earth, the Old Ones came from a great planet. In the myths and legends of many ancient civilizations they are known today as gods. These Old Ones call to me now, and I know that I'll soon be home with them. They had brought with them from their planet their great Rods of Power which were operated by their Minds. There was a current of a substance like electricity which passed from their foreheads to the Rod and the Rod would amplify this electricity, producing the desired effect intended by the operator. We cannot do this today because we have lost, through human evolution, the connecting tissue between the pineal and the pituitary glands in the head. However, in their heads, this connection produced a natural psychic ability. To them, this ability was perfectly normal. They were born with this connection and they used their abilities as we would use any of our five senses.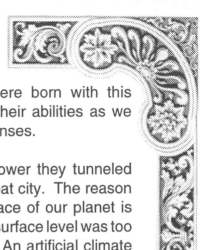

"With the Rods of Power they tunneled into the earth and built a great city. The reason they went beneath the surface of our planet is because the atmosphere at surface level was too dense for them to breathe. An artificial climate was created to sustain life, which has existed until this very day."

She paused, looking at me to see if I understood. Seeing that I listened and recorded well, she proceeded. I had learned not to question Anelleh while she was in the middle of her stories long ago. Not that I wasn't as curious as the next person, but so much of what she told me was, in time, to be fully provable. She had lived, after all, much longer than anyone I knew!

Closing her eyes again, she concentrated deeply and, somehow, I felt she was recalling something she actually lived, sometime... somewhere...

"The wise, ancient leader of these people who came in their silver ships was called simply 'Auuram'. It was a name toned rather than spoken as our names are spoken. The names of all in their civilization were toned. It was very beautiful..."

She hesitated and opened her eyes. I sensed the beauty she was 'seeing'.

"My child, I was told a very long time ago that there were fourteen secret places on our planet which serve as entrances into this magnificent city where the Old Ones live. Over the many millions of years of its existence, the inhabitants have sought to make it more beautiful, and now it is a city filled with Light Beams which emit beautiful rainbows! Few mortals have ever seen this city... I am one who has seen, been permitted to return to the outer world, and has remained silent about this for over two hundred years!"

Reaching for a glass of water, she rested for a few moments. Then, with her voice lowered a little, she continued...

"On the west coast of this land, in what is now southern California, there is a magnificent mountain. I was a young girl of about eighteen when I traveled to that mountain. Even in the summer, the lofty peaks are snow-laden. Of course it was not considered 'respectable' for a young woman to travel alone in those days, but I did! It wasn't easy emotionally or physically. There were Indians around the sacred mountain. They knew it was a holy place, but didn't know why. Even the valley around the mountain was

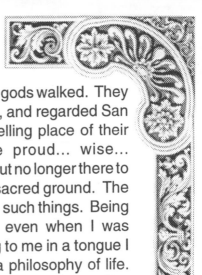

hallowed ground, where their gods walked. They were such a beautiful people, and regarded San Jacinto Mountain as the dwelling place of their Great Spirit. They were proud... wise... compassionately spiritual... but no longer there to protect what was once their sacred ground. The white men do not understand such things. Being black, I understood more... even when I was young. My mother, speaking to me in a tongue I only faintly remember, had a philosophy of life. It's part of my philosophy now. She said that 'The purpose of men and women was to grow. As the physical body grows and develops, it shows us the way our spiritual growth must take. The very reason we are here is to be as good and as perfect as possible. Our experiences in life lead us to this destiny...' Yes, my mother told me these things and I remember them still. She was a big woman, you know. Her smile and her eyes... there was always understanding in both."

She sighed and reached out for my hand. It was as if she was looking at her mother at that moment when she looked at me... releasing my hand, she lightly patted a tear from her face, then smiled... it was all right.

"I had fallen asleep not far from the base of the mountain. After only a few hours of rest, I was awakened... opening my eyes, I could scarcely believe what I saw... a tall, commanding man wearing a flowing cape of the deepest blue, trimmed with a narrow golden braid. In a peaceful voice he said to me..."

"Be at peace, Anelleh. You are loved. I mean you no harm."

"I was on my feet in seconds! There was no fear. This man had a presence that I have never felt or seen since."

"I am Auuram, Anelleh. We are pleased that you responded to our call to come and learn. Will you come with me for a little while?"

"He had read my thoughts and my heart. Reaching out for my hand, contact was made between us and I felt a wave-like vibration all over my body. My eyes automatically closed. Seconds later, we were no longer at my camp site, but in a huge carved out cavern that had cryptic symbols and painted pictures of magnificent artistry covering the walls."

The old woman opened her eyes for a moment, looking around her bedroom. It was as if to confirm that she was still in her room physically, as the reliving of the experience was quite vivid. Softly closing her eyes, she continued...

"The temperature was very comfortable in this cavern and the air seemed to me considerably purer. I remember pinching my arm to confirm I

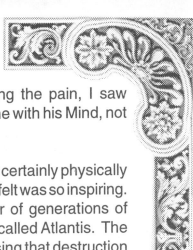

was there physically! Feeling the pain, I saw Auuram smile. He spoke to me with his Mind, not with speech, saying..."

"Anelleh, you are most certainly physically here, inside the mountain you felt was so inspiring. I am the Guide and Teacher of generations of descendants from my planet called Atlantis. The Wise Ones of the planet, sensing that destruction from terrible warfare was very near , evacuated those who were called Children of the Light Beam. We set our course toward Earth. It was so long ago that we made a home for ourselves within the planet. Some of our numbers decided to stay on the surface after getting used to the denser atmosphere, beginning to enjoy the fruits of Earth. Soon they scattered over the surface. With the passing of generations, they forgot their heavenly origins, and their lifespan soon decreased to only a few hundred years, as recorded in your Bible. Indeed, many of the events in the Holy Books of Earth record our coming and what happened to us. Some accounts in your Bible are literal and some are symbolic... those who remained in this mountain and in the underground cities have enjoyed extremely long lives. Many are still here, after thousands of years! Some willingly chose to leave their bodies, reincarnating on Earth when they were needed, becoming great Teachers to those on the surface."

"I seemed to understand everything that Auuram spoke, even the concept that we do not die but reincarnate again was very familiar and comfortable. I guess I was thinking very intently because I didn't even hear or see the woman who was now by our side. Seeing her brought me from my thoughts..."

"'This is Rahula, my sister,' was the thought I received. I don't think I've ever seen a more beautiful woman... she, too, spoke with her thoughts and lovingly welcomed me, saying that I was expected and all was in readiness. By now I could believe anything! They both looked at each other and smiled, reading my thoughts! Auuram left us and I began to walk quietly with Rahula to the end of the large cavern through an arched doorway of beautiful design. A short distance away was a small chamber which led to a sparkling pool."

"'Disrobe and bathe yourself, dear Sister.' I did."

"In looking back now, I realize that the outer world vibrations had to be cleansed from my aura so I would be completely ready for what was to occur.

"Little One, the water in the pool was unlike any water ever felt... I can only compare it with what liquid satin or silk would feel like. It was

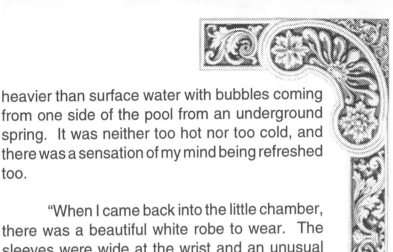

heavier than surface water with bubbles coming from one side of the pool from an underground spring. It was neither too hot nor too cold, and there was a sensation of my mind being refreshed too.

"When I came back into the little chamber, there was a beautiful white robe to wear. The sleeves were wide at the wrist and an unusual twisted golden cord was to be placed around the waist. About six inches of golden ribbon was at the hem of the garment. Next to the robe was a crystal pendant of unusual shape, suspended from a gold chain with unusual links. I'd not seen, much less worn, such clothing before that day! What was also unusual about the robe was that the fabric, while very silk-like, was extremely sturdy in addition to having no visible seams. I wondered how the garment was made...

"Rahula entered and, smiling, saw my delight with the robe. There was such Love coming from her. Extending her hand to me, she bid me to follow her. We walked further down the hallway, which was also carved from the living rock, and I remember admiring the symbols painted upon the walls. I asked my guide what the symbols were and her thoughts flowed to me that I would understand very soon, and to be patient. I was escorted Into another vast chamber, much larger than the first one I had visited with Auuram. Even now, Little One, the sight of over two hundred people looking at me with such Love was one of comfort and security..."

Placing her hand over mine at this point, my teacher seemed to want to emphasize that what was to be said next was very important. She transmitted a quietness in her speech and I inwardly knew that what was to be said next was to tell me much more about this extraordinary woman...

"Each of the two hundred people in the cavern was dressed in a garment similar to mine, but the colors varied. As I was to understand later, each was dressed in a robe befitting their spiritual progress.

"The walls in this cavern were magnificently carved - very smooth and painted with symbols. But what attracted my attention immediately was a very large sun disc which was expertly carved into the wall directly opposite me. Rays of pure gold and crystal flowed from the disc and seemed to be alive with color and vitality - pulsating with life! Standing directly under the great disc, emitting as much pure Light Energy as the disc itself, was Auuram. His arms were outstretched to greet me, and in a powerful voice he spoke..."

"Anelleh, speak to your family!"

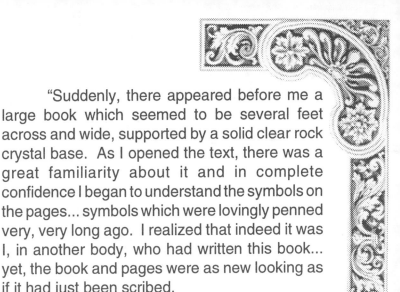

"Suddenly, there appeared before me a large book which seemed to be several feet across and wide, supported by a solid clear rock crystal base. As I opened the text, there was a great familiarity about it and in complete confidence I began to understand the symbols on the pages... symbols which were lovingly penned very, very long ago. I realized that indeed it was I, in another body, who had written this book... yet, the book and pages were as new looking as if it had just been scribed.

"The language I was reading was from the destroyed planet Atlantis, the same symbols that were carved and painted throughout the underground complex. But my Inner Eye was now opened and I understood! Aloud, I began reading the beautiful Laws given through inspiration to our ancient Wise Ones. I read the account of the migration from the planet to Earth and how the planet Atlantis was destroyed by their civilization, who had used their great Mind Power for destructive ends because it was easier and the results quicker in manifesting. I realize now, after two centuries, that we are again on that course, this time on Earth, but much will happen to intervene as many good souls from the ancient planet have incarnated on the surface world to help in these troubled times.

"After completing what was given to me to read, with humility I closed the great book and looked at Auuram and those gathered, to hear the Laws and the story of the migration. Auuram walked toward me and, placing both hands upon my shoulders, said very softly..."

"My beloved child, you have returned home after many aeons of time, and you have done well. We are pleased with what you have learned in many embodiments. Your soul has been purified by the trials of the body, mind and spirit."

"In that state of increased Awareness, there was a realization that I was truly Auuram's child from very long ago...

"Taking his hands from my shoulders, he stepped back a few steps and Rahula came forward with an unusual crown of purest gold. Auuram continued to speak..."

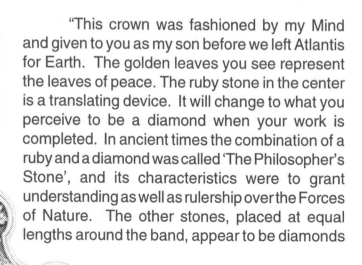

"This crown was fashioned by my Mind and given to you as my son before we left Atlantis for Earth. The golden leaves you see represent the leaves of peace. The ruby stone in the center is a translating device. It will change to what you perceive to be a diamond when your work is completed. In ancient times the combination of a ruby and a diamond was called 'The Philosopher's Stone', and its characteristics were to grant understanding as well as rulership over the Forces of Nature. The other stones, placed at equal lengths around the band, appear to be diamonds

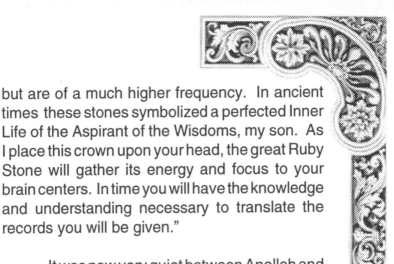

but are of a much higher frequency. In ancient times these stones symbolized a perfected Inner Life of the Aspirant of the Wisdoms, my son. As I place this crown upon your head, the great Ruby Stone will gather its energy and focus to your brain centers. In time you will have the knowledge and understanding necessary to translate the records you will be given."

It was now very quiet between Anelleh and me. At least an hour passed before she continued to speak. I've learned to respect another's quiet time... in retrospect I know that the little things I remember are often the most important to my life now...

"Auuram was my father on Atlantis and I had come home! It was a magnificent moment... just at that realization, soaring music flowed through the cavern. It was music from an instrument neither constructed nor played by human hand. It came in waves... and waves... of beauty... it came from those assembled... from their very hearts! Can you imagine what the sound vibration of pure Love is?

"I spent the night and most of the next day with my family and then returned with Auuram to the campsite the same way I departed.

"Little One, I went back to the mountain only a few more times in my physical body but many times in my Light Body."

Reaching into the drawer by a large table next to her bed, Anelleh carefully removed two items. One was a deep purple, soft velvet bag of good size. The other was what looked like a hand written manuscript. Her hand was trembling a little when she had both items on her lap. Great care and respect were given to both items. Opening the velvet bag first, I saw before me the crown! The Ruby was missing from the middle because in its place was what appeared to be a large diamond of unspeakable brilliance. Rays actually flowed from it! Anelleh's face showed as much surprise as mine when she looked at the diamond. Carefully, she placed the crown upon her head and a great peace descended upon us both. Her attention then focused on the manuscript lying in her lap. It was about nine inches thick and about a foot long, all written in her own hand.

"Over 175 years ago, on my second journey physically into the mountain, I was given a manuscript book to translate into English. The original was very large, much like the one I described earlier to you, however, the content was different. During that trip into the mountain, I stayed with my family for seven years, living with the Brothers and Sisters in harmony. I learned about the Universal Laws of Life and how these Laws govern all levels of existence at all times. Those who have a deeper understanding of the

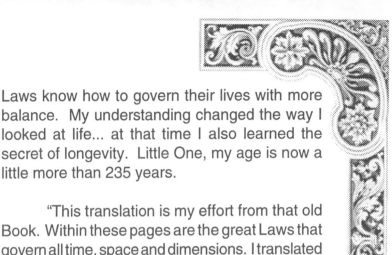

Laws know how to govern their lives with more balance. My understanding changed the way I looked at life... at that time I also learned the secret of longevity. Little One, my age is now a little more than 235 years.

"This translation is my effort from that old Book. Within these pages are the great Laws that govern all time, space and dimensions. I translated from picture-like symbols which were penned by the ancient Atlanteans that I once belonged to, so long ago. My child, I have tried, in my own way, to teach you some of these Laws and I am pleased with your growth. This manuscript is yours now... know this - that you will be asked how these records were translated. Say that it was with an Inner Intelligence and perception in combination with the Ruby Stone, the translation device. You will be asked what the records looked like - say that they were not a book but rather a series of seven hundred sheets of the purest alchemical gold; very thin and paper-like but entirely durable. The glyphs were written into the gold. Some of the glyphs were pictures and in color. Never have I seen such an interesting form of pictorial communication.

"You will be asked to produce the original volume. The translation must speak for itself for the volume is safe in the deepest Inner Cities close to the inner sanctuaries inside the mountain. Child, these are the records for the race of humanity now being born. What is not understood by men and women at this time will be understood in the future... for my people are now coming back.

"I have known great peace and knowledge since the day this was given to me. Now, while I am preparing to take my place for a while with my father in the mountain, I have tried to teach you to continue in my place, if you so choose by your own free will. Should you wish to continue, you will be called into the mountain and taught, as I... you will see me there. Child, my Peace I give to you this day..."

Then, placing both of her hands upon my head, she gave me what I felt to be an ancient blessing in some unknown language. I can only say that I felt it, yet did not mentally understand it. Now I do understand it, as I have some of the Inner knowledge, as Anelleh had Inner knowledge.

Long moments passed. I looked at her through tears. Her body had taken on a golden glow... a beauty that I'd never seen before. Music... yes, there was music but I didn't know where it was coming from until there was a realization that it was the same music Anelleh heard long ago from the very hearts of those who loved her! I also felt I was Awakening to something I knew... reaching out her two arms, she whispered...

"I return to the Infinite Divine Source of All!"

With those words, she went through her physical transition. At that instant the crown she wore faded from her head and seemed to follow her to where she was going...

I had a lump in my throat. This old woman had been my beloved Teacher for seven years but it had seemed like a lifetime. Because of her advanced age she had no family. I was the only one she had to make the last arrangements. Her directions were to be cremated. It was done.

Anelleh had very few possessions. A few pieces of furniture, clothing and appliances. In giving away these items to those who were in need, I came upon a very old wooden box which she had hidden in the recesses of a dresser. Carved symbols adorned this box, which was about six inches square. I opened it.

Inside was a white silk piece of fabric which was tinged with the yellow of age. The silk sheltered a glowing crystal pendant, suspended on an unusual gold chain! The same one Anelleh wore on her first trip into the mountain... I placed it around my neck and immediately felt the warmth of my dear Teacher... there was a knowing that she left the necklace for me to find... and in finding it, adorning myself with it, the mountain then called to me...

I reflected on all that Anelleh had said to me, and in my very being, I knew what the course of my life must be... so many questions were in my mind since her passing... what was my relationship in the past with her?... was I, too, a part of her ancient planet?... If I walked her Path, would I accept the many sacrifices and responsibilities?

Everything Within me sang! Yes! I heard the music again, and in my Mind's Eye, I saw dear Anelleh's face smile with a tenderness... I reached out for her... still learning... this Little One is still learning.

THE SECOND

PORTAL

SHALIMAR

...A dream...

I feel like I am once again the little boy so long ago when I remember a vivid dream that I wanted to come true!... And I haven't really considered dreaming since the sparkling eyes of that youngster in me 'ooed' and 'aaahed' at the sight of his first bicycle. It seemed strange to have a 'wish' at this time of life...

"Wishing is for children, and certainly not very mature! **Work** for what you want! Get educated! Get the right job! Marry... have children... a nice house and - above all - join the country club to meet others as potentially influential as yourself! That's what is important to succeed!"

As he looked around his home, all was in order... everything was as it should be - neatly ordered, as was his life. A feeling of sadness closed in on the man... for what good was all the success without someone special to share it with... where was the companion who knew and understood him and with whom he could love so very much - a person to bring the first flower of Spring to and a person to just...?

Silence... thoughts interrupted and the wordthoughts halted... there was a HUSH in the room. A tingling, warm feeling was overcoming his senses. "My, oh my... what thoughts you've been traveling through!" Eyes blinking as if to be certain that she was there - no mistaking it! It was Shalimar!

Eyes brighter than all the twinkling stars... hair silver-white and braided with fresh pastel flowers and a forehead that shone with the brilliance of a thousand crystal gems! In Thinkspeak, the wondrous beauty focused on the man... "And I thought for a moment I had been forgotten! Come with me, my friend... to a place where you need to go to find your dream!"

Flashthoughts raced through his brain! Shalimar! The friend of his boyhood... the companion that traveled with him to imaginary places where learning and play continually were intertwined! Whenever he was sad and alone, Shalimar would enter, just to the right of his most precious dreams - poof! So many cycles of time

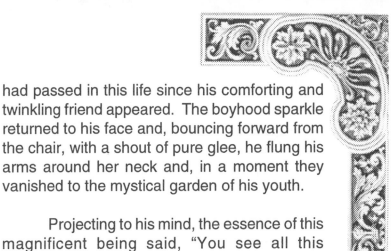

had passed in this life since his comforting and twinkling friend appeared. The boyhood sparkle returned to his face and, bouncing forward from the chair, with a shout of pure glee, he flung his arms around her neck and, in a moment they vanished to the mystical garden of his youth.

Projecting to his mind, the essence of this magnificent being said, "You see all this wonderment again, my dear one... but as a man - with eyes and heart that have been saddened by the weight of loneliness which does not have to be... look around you! This is the garden you and I created together when you were only five years old... a place to learn and to play - a place to have all your questions answered. Come... walk with me again. Think not of the questions, but look around you for the answers!"

His head was on her shoulder, resting on the abundance of fine, snowy hair... slowly walking with his arm around her graceful neck... Answers... "I don't even know what I really want! The questions aren't formed yet!" Thinking... thinking... "But she said to look **around** for the answers... what shall I look for... everything's beautiful here... Ah, the stream I used to play in... the meadow and the gaily colored flowers I used to lie in, looking upward to the icy blue sky, Shalimar resting by my side... sometimes letting me put my head on her shoulder... sweeter memories one could never imagine... where did that sense of security go?

"Isn't this what I've always wanted?   A peaceful place... space, a loving presence who is Love itself? Is there such a wondrous place in the world I really live in? Is there someone to love me? Is there... questions! Again... she said to look for the **answers**!"

The man's thoughts were interrupted by the gentle thought-insertion of Shalimar..."My friend, **look around you**! This peace is of YOUR creation! I only showed you the Way here... leading you always to the Door of your own Truth. If this garden were not already in your Soul, it would not have manifested! Do you see... you need only to create your peace, to select it, focus it and then claim it! Claim the golden thoughts you think! Claim the majesty of your own Love, unlocking all doors, tearing down all walls, not being afraid to claim what has been yours always!

"Your paramind has already created all the buildings you will ever design... has traveled to all places you've ever been... has even loved all those you will ever love! It's all there - like the treasure chest buried deeply within the indigo forest beckoning for the Truth to come to expose the pulsating gems of Truth to the crashing rays of the day!"

Shalimar's eyes glowed with great Light..." Man, rise thyself now and come with me..." and fading from this garden of dreams, they again

110

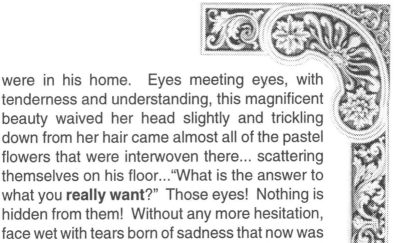

were in his home. Eyes meeting eyes, with tenderness and understanding, this magnificent beauty waived her head slightly and trickling down from her hair came almost all of the pastel flowers that were interwoven there... scattering themselves on his floor..."What is the answer to what you **really want**?" Those eyes! Nothing is hidden from them! Without any more hesitation, face wet with tears born of sadness that now was totally leaving, he said, "I want to be in love and to know the truth of that love." With a whisperthought, Shalimar responded, "As you have spoken the answer, so it is to pass... save the flowers, O Man... you will see my Unicorn Eyes again soon, shining through the love-eyes of the one you seek. The singleness of love within you will draw that Essence to you in unexpected ways. I will touch you again, beloved Man... forever have I shown you The Way and The Light, leading you to the Portal of your Dreams... I am the Eternal Yah of God... that which is the Unicorn Consciousness. I lead you to the Door that you may pass through alone and unafraid. To you now, that door is marked LOVE and many come approaching the steps but dare not proceed further, unable to give what LOVE expects to receive. When you can climb the steps marked "compassion... unselfishness... giving" and pass through the blazing Portal that purifies, I'll be waiting for you beyond the Gates, playing in the Dream Garden of your Soul, forever in love... without restricting walls or enclosures of judgment to bind you to ignorance. I will show you a freedom you've not thought possible! I have always loved you, O Man... forever will I keep my Promise to The Source of All to bring Loving Joy to thee."

Eyes glittering Love to the man, the radiant Shalimar turned slightly to the right and there was the flaming Portal of pulsating Blue and Golden Light. She walked towards and through it... pausing between the columns, looking back briefly at the man. The word "courage" impressed upon his mind at that instant... the entire scene fading as the dream decrystalized... poof!

He turned to his worktable. Upon it was a new drawing for a home... a home of the future... translucent, airy and beautiful! The flowers from Shalimar's mane appeared around the house drawing, encircling the home with a fragrance of wood flowers... flash! For the first time, the man KNEW THAT HE KNEW and with great energy, ideas... ideas like fountains of gushing water, flowed from his Mind! The house came alive under several more hours of work! The ideas now incorporated into this house could and WOULD change the way people of Earth lived in their dwellings forever!

THE DOOR

...*T*he longing in her heart to find the Doorway was more intense now than ever. When her eyes were closed, there it was... **The Door**... but it was so far into the horizon. Trying to walk there, even in consciousness, made it seem even farther away - melding sometimes into the mountains that were on the far side of **The Door**. Accumulated thoughts... pieces of knowledge tripping through the brain did not bring her Path closer to this Portal.

Wisdom, born of unscrambling the piece-bit information from Ages past, only made the longing to enter that much more intense... Loving so honestly, and yet rarely receiving that honesty in return, made the Voyage sadder but richer.

Now, the Soul... a-l-o-n-e... stands viewing the plainscape ahead... all in all is dropped behind her... all that she understood is now emptied at the Altar of Truth. She thought she had Truth... but if so, wouldn't **The Door** be there... wide open for her, permitting Right of Passage to the Loving Unknown One?

All has fallen away... only bodyessence, Soulessence remains - the Truth of who she **is** stood on the plainscape. Blond, silver hair and violet eyes, pale skin draped in violet sheer silk, revealing the true body curved beneath... nothing of Earth must remain so that the Focus of lifetimes can now be pierced... **THE DOOR!** Ahead, stepping firmly but slowly, she went. Around all consciousness were past thoughts of "...what will they do without me?" and then the question/ answer ..."Ah, but what will I do without **Me**?" ... pressing forward, soul bent now into the wind of heart pain... yet, **The Door** seemed to be closer - nearer than it had ever been... the windpain was heavier now and Light thoughts of what would or could have been if the Path now taken were not approached so many lifetimes ago. Were the choices good? What **IS** good? Is anything really bad? Being there, in the presentness, is all that can be considered now. Good? Yes. It is all God the Good.

Walking against the Truthwind she must be singleEyed... singleminded and wanting to pass through that **Door** so badly that nothing else mattered, and yet... there was not the understanding of **what** was **behind The Door**... only knowing that it **must be reached** for "...what will I do without **Me**?" ...Thoughts going, coming around, through, over, under - no place where the thoughtquestions were not... then, immediately, swiftly and with a totality of completion,

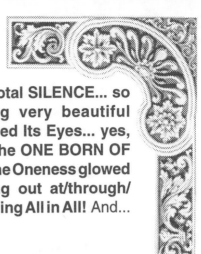

all stopped... SILENCE. Total SILENCE... so profound that something very beautiful happened. The Soul Opened Its Eyes... yes, Eyes! Not just ONE, but the ONE BORN OF THE MANY... everywhere, the Oneness glowed and the I/Eye was looking out at/through/above/below and in everything All in All! And... there was The Door!

Seven steps... yes... she counted seven to the first plateau. They were very clear, pale blue... transparent with the mist of time radiating out from them. Slowly, with Force of Will, she approached the plateau. Pale blue, blending, softly into violet. Then three steps. Slowly again she ascended... one... two... three and there was **The Door, carved with scenes of exactly what she had just been through! Outlining everything - there it all was! Written exactly at the moment she had just lived it, culminating with her looking at The Door in amazement! It was the Scroll of her Life at that very moment, written in Essencecrystal, pulsating with Life!**

Touching **The Door**... slowly, carefully, it opened from the center inward so that walking between these two pulsating carved Doors was now happening... the heart Within beating hard... **this was the moment**... all other Doors had been passed and this was the last into a **Light** that she understood with feelings of Soul. But now, with Eyes of Soul, Heart of Hearts and Mind of Universal

Mind - for on the other side of **The Door** was...
herSelf!   Ahhhhhhh... there was the knowing
now... that which was the GodLove within the
Universal Heart, the Love of the Self in all its
flowing into pain, suffering, misunderstandings
and sorrows, was now blended into the Elixir of
Love itSelf!

Looking at one another, beyond **The Door**,
they, with Eyes of violetfire and Love Within,
slowly walked toward each other and embraced...
dissolving, flowing and melding into each other...
no longer two but One.

It was all so very simple and could have
happened so long ago! Turning, she faced **The
Door**, and saw that it had dissolved. In its place
was a singular pink rose, in the fullest expression
of its flowering, emitting a perfume of Joy! Ahead?
There was yet one Love to flow into before flowing
into the Oneness of **The Source**... one last Love
who is also complete and has crossed through
The Door to himSelf... waiting, waiting... being
there.

MY SONG

My Song was written as a birthday present

for my beloved

Sister of Light,

Mary Bassano of Kissimmee, Florida

on the occasion of her birthday

a few years ago.

May all of Mary's birthdays

be enchanted!

*M*y heart was heavy with the loss of a loved one. Months had passed and still my smile was forced and people who used to invite me to lunch now realized they had other appointments. I was not good company for them or myself. My 61st birthday had passed recently with barely one or two friends remembering. Sometimes the feeling that invisibility flooded my soul was becoming more apparent to me..." My God!," I would cry aloud many nights,..." Why do You still keep me here? For what purpose? Free me and take me to YourSelf!" ...even God, quite literally, saw through me. I felt forgotten in my Soul...

...and then the event happened...

When I was a child of about seven years old, my father had given me a bamboo flute on my birthday... such joy it gave me with its pleasant melodies! Throughout my life I kept it with me... sometimes playing it and feeling its very soft wood. In all these years it was a friend to me... It was to that little flute that I turned at a time when my soul was so saddened... I placed it in front of me on an old pink velvet cloth that it always snuggled within when not in use... and just closed my eyes for a while. My hands were on my lap with the flute on the table... my sadness was overwhelming and tears came easily, but I remained still, even through the tears. I heard my flute!! The melody was solitary and sad... it WAS my flute, but I wasn't playing it! Opening my eyes quickly, I saw the old Chinese instrument in front of me... it hadn't moved and yet the Breath of God echoed through it... singing to me... higher and higher were the notes with melodies that warmed me, enriched me and caused me great joy... a feeling that had been forgotten! My heart was playing this flute... God through my heart spoke... all of the laughter, joy and contentment as a child welled Within me as the flute danced its melody... my melody... my Soul's song!

To this day, I have never been given to understand how the flute sang to me, just sitting on my table... but the harmonic melodies healed my Soul... forever! Even after I died, my melody was surrounding me and I was able to give my gift of joy away...

And my gift to you? Why, it's right in front of you! May I give you my precious bamboo flute so that your sacred Soul melody can play for you, to heal you? Yes... close your eyes and there it will be - the humble instrument which even now, as my words are whispered in your ear, is resounding through your private universe with The Song of The Source. Listen softly and even

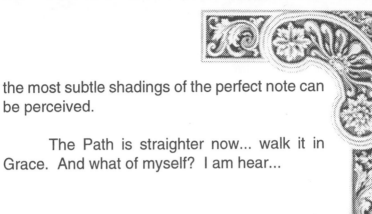

the most subtle shadings of the perfect note can be perceived.

The Path is straighter now... walk it in Grace. And what of myself? I am hear...

The King

of

The Dolphins

This magical story was written

at the request of my dear friend,

Beatrice de Borbon of Miami, Florida.

Beatrice was planning to publish

a magnificent new magazine

named "B de B", and asked me

to write a story about a dolphin.

The King of the Dolphins

was the loving result.

As of this printing, "B de B" has not gone

to press with its premier edition, and

therefore it is with the loving and gracious

permission of Beatrice that this story is

included here.

Thank You, Dear Beatrice!

An Ancient Faerie Tale to Remember....

T here was a hush over the Valley of the Blue Moon on a planet not so far away... an air of expectancy of an exciting event that everyone on Venus awaited with hearts that were pure and open. Far away, beyond the northern sands that kissed the water as it gently played with little shells deposited from distant places, a melody was heard... enchanting... heart quickening with levels of love... chords that inspired ancient visions of far memories.

We were all there... you and I! We stood at the shoreline of the Valley of the Blue Moon that was adjacent to the capital city of Venus, called Vera Oona. This was a day of great importance for it was the day of the coming of the Dolphin King himself! We all awaited the one we called "Dolphus" for he was to teach us, the Children of Vera Oona, about the water kingdom and how to play with all life in the great pale blue waters surrounding Vera Oona. The music became clearer and we could feel the magical energy inside us, swirling and moving with joy, joy, joy! We literally "saw" the colors of the music and, with a great burst of energy, Dolphus came near the shore and greeted us. We all came into his watery domain and he played with us as if he were a child himself. We all knew he was very ancient in age and yet his energy abounded and exploded with youth! Small angels attended Dolphus from the watery kingdom and rode upon his back as well as hovering above his great body. "My children of the earthly domain, come closer to me and allow my angel friends to place upon your foreheads a magical Seal of Remembering that will enable me to take you to my splendid kingdom not too far from here, beneath the pale blue waters, a Seal of Remembering that will permit you to breathe the oxygen from the water for a brief time. I have a teaching to impart to your souls that you will remember at a future time... far, far into the future on a distant planet in this solar system!"

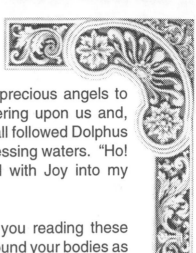

We all permitted the precious angels to place the Seal of Remembering upon us and, with an Inner thrill of joy, we all followed Dolphus into the warm, clear and caressing waters. "Ho! We go forward, Inward and with Joy into my kingdom, little ones!"

I **know** that each of you reading these words can 'feel' the water around your bodies as the Seal of Remembering is, even now, being reactivated by the faerie kingdom, for we felt the water slide by us... feeling like water infused with the essence of silk itself. Schools of radiant fish came over to us and seemed to 'talk' with us, trees of multi-colored coral swayed with the water currents as our bodies moved past them, almost waving a friendly greeting.

There it was! Straight ahead! Dolphus slowed his pace so that we could see his kingdom. Radiant! Sparkling! Vivid with crystalline colors! Dolphus turned to us and, mentally imparted the wondrous tale of how this underwater kingdom of shining spheres, cubes, and pyramidal shapes were placed there by the residents of Vera Oona on the surface in a direct working relationship with the members of the dolphin kingdom. He told that one day, he visited a man sitting on the shore and began a long relationship with him of exchanging knowledge and the wisdom that great age had brought to both of them. Before the man died, he asked Dolphus if he and others on Vera

Oona could materialize liquid crystal geometric forms and present them to Dolphus to create a sparkling council area beneath the seas where he and others within the dolphin civilization could meet, discuss and learn from each other and from humankind.

"Come, my children, sit upon any of the radiant shapes and we will speak of a time in the future when each of you will remember this sacred meeting between kingdoms, remembering my messages sent to the Heart of your Soul so that you will **know** the hidden and secret ways to communicate with **all** lines of evolution... species of the air, the water, those roaming on the earth. We are beings that cause you to remember your purpose as part of the human line of evolution... we look at you with deep and abiding Eyes of Soul to shake you into a far memory of the lives that we all danced together with JOY in our hearts and communicated freely, never a thought of hurting each other for any reason. Be still now, my children of the upper world of earth; hear my thoughts and focus well on the pictures I am now going to send to you of a far off twilight time on another planet far into the future where you will take a lifetime and find that the kingdoms are at war with one another, not at peace."

How Dolphus caused us to see what were events thousands of years into the future I cannot tell you. What you and I saw that magical day set

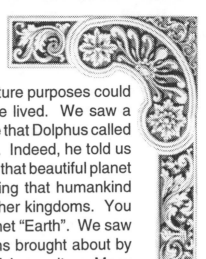

forever in our hearts what future purposes could be for us at a time yet to be lived. We saw a beautiful blue planet in space that Dolphus called "Saras", meaning "Sorrows". Indeed, he told us that "Saras" was the name of that beautiful planet because of all of the suffering that humankind placed upon itself and all other kingdoms. You and I now call this same planet "Earth". We saw the chaos between kingdoms brought about by the disordered thoughts of humanity. Many beautiful birds now were birds of prey and fed upon small members of the animal kingdom. Beautiful and majestic felines fed upon other mammals... and on it went, kingdom after kingdom in chaos because humanity chose the road of indifference toward all life. No harmony. No. peace. No communication between kingdoms and no help between kingdoms.

Bells! We all began to hear the tinkling of sparkling little bells! Angel bells! "Look up, my children, into the skies of your dream vision of your future!" Our eyes floating upward, we saw iridescent streams of rainbows flowing all over the earth! Into every body of water... oceans, rivers, streams and waterfalls, and flowing on every inch of land, the streams of rainbows arched. They flooded humankind, the beasts of the fields, forests and glens. This energy flowed directly from the Mind and Heart of the One Source called God, to every species in every kingdom, renewing the ancient promise of LIFE! Angels, using the twinkling rainbow rays like happy toys, slid down the rays and began to walk among mankind and beast alike, teaching the LAW OF THE ONE!

Dolphus was quiet for a while... waiting for our dream vision to solidify in our minds. Singing! We heard the most haunting, serene melodies from our ancient friend Dolphus. He was singing into our very Soul the ancient melody that connected all kingdoms together. When we began to open our eyes, we saw that there was a swirling iridescent, pulsating energy from Dolphus' heart and as it radiated and swirled forward, it touched our hearts and our hearts mirrored our energy to him. We were ONE... all of us. We all felt his tremendous age mixed with invigorated youth and the massive wisdom stored within his Soul. Ah, what treasures he could teach us that would be beyond the price of the greatest gemstones!

Softly, we heard within our Soul, "All Life is ONE and inter-connected. This is a great Universal Law of UNITY. Take this teaching with you, my children, into the far off time in the future when you all will be called upon to teach this simple Truth... ALL LIFE IS ONE AND INTER-CONNECTED." We had the knowing that it was now time to return to the ivory colored powdered sands of the beach of Vera Oona. Flowing upward and, again, the glistening pale blue silk water flowing on all sides of our bodies, we were

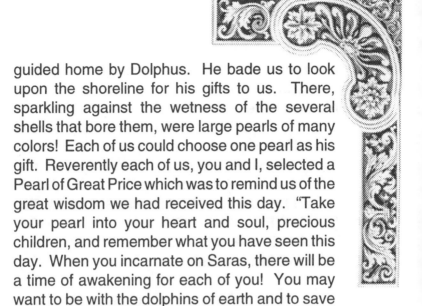

guided home by Dolphus. He bade us to look upon the shoreline for his gifts to us. There, sparkling against the wetness of the several shells that bore them, were large pearls of many colors! Each of us could choose one pearl as his gift. Reverently each of us, you and I, selected a Pearl of Great Price which was to remind us of the great wisdom we had received this day. "Take your pearl into your heart and soul, precious children, and remember what you have seen this day. When you incarnate on Saras, there will be a time of awakening for each of you! You may want to be with the dolphins of earth and to save them from further harm. You may have the Seal of Remembrance activated again and you will have a sure and definite understanding of your purpose... to educate all of humankind in the **LAW OF ONE** and that every creature and human being is interconnected. Teach, my children! Teach!"

In a sunlit splash of energy, our beloved Dolphus vanished. I have my Pearl of Great Price... I know that you picked up your beautiful pearl... some of you picked up pale blue ones, some iridescent peach and pink. Still others saw some with a green tint and loved them very much. Hold out your hands now... yes, you who are reading this faerie tale... you were on the beaches of Vera Oona with me that very day with Dolphus, the King of the Dolphins and in your hands now outstretched before you is the energy of that pearl you picked up on the beach on Venus so... long... ago. Place it in your heart... I'll wait.............. Ah, the peace and purposeful energy it gives will open up for you, as in the very ancient past, the Seal of Remembrance so that you and I can, once again, dance with Dolphus in the pale blue waters and remember why we came to Earth... to **UPLIFT IT WITH JOY... WITH MUSIC... WITH LAUGHTER... AND WITH THE KNOWLEDGE THAT WE ARE ALL "ONE".... WE ARE ALL INTER-CONNECTED.**

"Wisdom" is the Pearl of Great Price and that was the gift of Dolphus....

Perhaps we will sit once again, you and I, and speak of legends that the faeries tell of so long ago and far away, and yet just a Seal of Remembrance away! May the iridescence of each of the rays of the rainbow touch each of you who read these words...

COMING SOON!

THE AKASHIC RECORDS
by Roberta S. Herzog, DD

If you enjoyed this book, don't miss the author's latest work, The Akashic Records. Based on twenty-two years experience as a reader of the Akashic Records, Dr. Herzog gives us an inside view of the etheric libraries for Earth and other planets in this solar system, where the records of our lives and our planet are stored.

This rare and unusually beautiful publication will be available in a collectors edition as well as in softback. It is greatly enriched by the superb color pictures created by Brian Keeler, providing detailed visual access to these unseen worlds.

Learn about the path of the soul as it journeys through time and many incarnations, and how we truly are a reflection of our thoughts, words and deeds.

This book is a must for all serious collectors of high quality esoteric literature.

For more information, please contact the publisher or enquire at your local bookstore. Publication is scheduled for Summer 1994.

Order Form

Discounts Available! Five or more books sent to the same address will earn you a 12% discount, exclusive of shipping and handling charges. Sales tax where applicable.

Please send _____ copies of Ancient Wizdom Stories
                                                          $ _____

_____

_____

_____

More than 6 boo

Telephone Num
Fax Number:

Please Print:

Name:_____
Address:_____
City:_____State:____Zip:_____

ANCIENT WIZDOM
STORIES

Roberta S. Herzog

Roberta S. Herzog has been an ardent student and teacher of the Ancient Wisdom Teachings for over thirty-five years. She is a gifted reader of *The Akashic Records* for the past twenty-two consecutive years, with a world-wide clientele. A consecrated Archbishop of The International Church of Ageless Wisdom, she has authored the Church's Seminary courses in addition to authoring *"Beauty Unknown"* and *"Legends of Anelleh"*. Dr. Herzog resides in the mountains of northeastern Pennsylvania. Her latest book, *"The Akashic Records"*, is due to be published in 1994.